Name: _____

Prd: _____

Hip-Hop, History & Ethics

Cultural Development (Student Workbook)

Brady Goodwin Jr.

The Urban Remix Project

From the MORE-ality series - Connecting Hip Hop to History and the Hereafter

Hip-Hop, History & Ethics:
Character Development + Cultural Development

ISBN 978-0-9884155-8-4

<u>Dedicated to the Students at Simon Gratz High School</u>

Special shout-out to:

Principal Bennett for allowing this program to be piloted with the Bulldogs

The Urban Family Council for opening the doors of character-education

Dr. Peter Teague and Lancaster Bible College for supporting this project

Table of Contents

Contents

What's It All About?

Back in the day, in 1988, rapper KRS-One said that Hip-Hop was too young to have any 'old-school' artists. But today, that's no longer the case. We get to celebrate Hip-Hop's exciting history while learning from some of the mistakes of the past.

This course is not just about music. It is about the life-styles and values represented in the music. This course is about helping to build character in youth and young adults who live in the communities where the lyrics to many songs are lived out.

As the rapper formerly known as Mos Def once said, Hip-Hop is not "some giant living in the hills somewhere. . . we are Hip-Hop. You, me . . . everybody. You wanna know what's gonna happen with Hip-Hop? Whatever's happening with us. Next time you ask yourself, where Hip-Hop is goin'. Ask yourself, 'where am I going? How am I doing?' Then you'll get a clear idea. [Because] Hip-Hop won't get better until people get better."

So, since 'better people' leads to a better culture, units 1 – 3 will focus on your personal character development. Then, units 4 – 7 will focus on Hip-Hop and cultural development. Even if Hip Hop is not your culture, you can still learn and use these principles to build your character and strengthen whatever culture you do identify with.

By the end of this course, you will be able to

- Contrast and Evaluate three ethical systems and decide which is most beneficial
- Identify the character traits needed to live consistently within your preferred ethical system

- Outline the historical pathway of the ethics of Hip-Hop culture by connecting Hip-Hop history to African American history
- Resolve to live and lead counter-culturally in areas where the destructive tendencies in the broader culture clash with your own values

Are you ready? Let's dive in!

Preliminary Lessons

- How Does Education Work?
- Old School vs. New
- Freestyle vs. Written

Agenda: To prepare for this course which looks at Hip Hop through an academic lens, it is important to understand how Education works. Many people spend years in primary and secondary education and have never asked the question, 'what does any of this have to do with life? My life? Or any of the things I really want to learn. So first we will answer those questions and then apply the answers to Hip Hop as a culture.

Student Learning Outcomes: By the end of this unit, you will be able to

- Use the term "cross-disciplinary" to explain how education works
- Use Hip Hop terminology as a metaphor for life

Preliminary Lesson 1 - How Does Your Education Work?

Consider the core classes, such as Math, English, Science and History, offered in a typical high school. What do you think those subjects have to do with one another? Or do you think they are all disconnected subjects with no relation between the four of them? Explain your answer.

_____

_____

_____

_____

_____

_____

_____

_____

Rate on a Scale from 1 to 5

Math _____

Science _____

History _____

English _____

Math: _____

Science: _____

_____

History: _____

_____

English: _____

_____

Preliminary Lesson 3 - Please Listen to My Demo

1. Hip Hop is
   a. A mindset   b. A music style   c. The same as Rap   d. A culture

2. On a scale from 1 – 5, how much do you think you know about Hip Hop history?

   1   2   3   4   5   (**1** being nothing at all, **5** being you could probably teach this class)

3. Who said, "Life ain't nuthin but B*tches and Money"
   a. Snoop Dogg   b. Ice Cube   c. Jay Z   d. Lil Wayne   e. Master P

4. The four geographical areas of Hip Hop in the United States are
   a. East Coast, West Coast, North Coast and South Coast
   b. East Coast, West Coast, Middle America and Bottom of the Map
   c. West Coast, East Coast, Dirty South and Mid-west

5. Using your answer from #2 - where did Hip Hop show up 1st, 2nd 3rd and 4th

   1st _____

   2nd _____

   3rd _____

   4th _____

6. When criticized for rapping about violence and shooting other black and brown men, most rappers respond by saying, "It's just entertainment, like what you see in the movies. If you're going to criticize me then criticize the movie industry too!" <u>Do you agree that it is the same thing or is rap different?</u> **Explain your answer?**

   _____

   _____

   _____

   _____

   _____

   _____

7. Turn and talk with someone about your answer to #4
   a. Who did you talk to? _____

   b. Did you and the person agree or disagree?

   _____

Watch the video of DMC (one-half of the legendary rap-group Run DMC), then answer the following questions

1. How many times does DMC curse in this video? _____

2. How many times does he use the N-word in this video? _____ Why do you think that is?

   _____
   _____
   _____

3. List two things that he says that you agree with?

   _____
   _____
   _____

4. Did he say anything that you disagree with? If so what and why do you disagree?

   _____
   _____
   _____
   _____
   _____
   _____

5. DMC produced this video at the age of 54, do you think his opinion should matter or does the next generation get to make Hip Hop whatever they want it to be? Explain

   _____
   _____
   _____

Watch the remainder of the video then answer the following questions.

8. What do you think DMC means by "recreating" Hip Hop?

   _____
   _____
   _____

9. If you could push the button to recreate it right now, would you? If so, what would be different about Hip Hop after you hit your button? If not, why not?

_____

_____

_____

10. What rappers would you keep and who would you dismiss (and why)?

_____

_____

_____

Preliminary Lesson 3: Freestyle or Written – The Original

Some rappers are good at writing very creative lyrics; we call them lyricists. There are also rappers who are good at rapping "off the top of their head," with no premeditation; we call that "freestyling." Just as there is a time for both, there are benefits and drawbacks to each approach.

Student Learning Outcomes: As a result of this lesson, I can

- Differentiate between Freestyled and Written raps
- Compare and Contrast the two, listing the pros and cons of each
- Decide when or in what situations each approach is most fitting

....

Intro

1. Which would you prefer more, to listen to someone rap freestyle or written? Explain why?

   _____

   _____

   _____

2. Share your answer with at least two other students. Briefly right down what they had to say.

   _____

   _____

   _____

   _____

Diving In - Distinguishing Marks

1. How could you tell whether a verse was Free-styled or Written? What are some difference between the two approaches?

Free-style	Written
1) _____	1) _____
2) _____	2) _____
3) _____	3) _____
4) _____	4) _____
5) _____	5) _____

2. In the following situations, should a rapper freestyle or use a written rhyme instead?

    a. _____

    b. _____

3. In August of 2009, the rapper Drake was brand new to the Hip Hop world. He was invited (at the last minute) to go on Funk Master Flex's Hot 97 radio show to freestyle. He went on air and delivered a great performance. What did most listeners think?

    a. Drake was rapping "off the top" of his head

    b. Drake was performing pre-written bars

    c. Drake had a ghost-writer

4. The next day, pictures surfaced of Drake in the Hot 97 studio, rapping while staring down at the smartphone in his hand. It was clear that Drake was not rapping "off the top" of his head. When rap fans criticized him for using "written" raps in what was thought to be a freestyle moment, what do you think Drake said in response?

    _____

5. Two take-aways from Drake's response

    1) _____

    2) _____

6. Just a couple of months later, in October at the BET Hip Hop Awards, Drake's label-mate Nicki Minaj found herself in a similar situation. In that year's cypher, Nicki rapped a verse that showed off her skills and blew fans away. But it was clear to most people that she was not "freestyling." When rap fans criticized her for using pre-written rhymes, what do you think Nicki said in response?

   _____

7. Two take-aways from Nicki's response

   1) _____

   2) _____

8. Crutches are _____ that rappers lean on for support when their freestyle is falling off; such as_____.

9. The more _____ a rapper has the less he/she will rely on crutches.

10. Which one do you think will be revisited and relevant over time such that people will still want to hear it ten years from now – something freestyled or something written? Explain why.

   _____

   _____

   _____

   _____

Outro

Can you tell?

1. _____ ☐ Good Written ☐ Wack Written ☐ Good Freestyle ☐ Wack Freestyle

2. _____ ☐ Good Written ☐ Wack Written ☐ Good Freestyle ☐ Wack Freestyle

REMIX!

Do you think that life is better as a "free-style" or as a "written"? **Explain why.**

_____

_____

_____

Diving In – On the Real

1. How could you tell if someone was freestyling their way through life or if they were living according to a written plan? What are some differences between the two?

Free-style	Written
1) _____	1) _____
2) _____	2) _____
3) _____	3) _____
4) _____	4) _____
5) _____	5) _____

2. Think of your life as one long verse. Based on #1 above, has your "life's verse" so far been more like a "freestyle" or a "written". **Explain** with examples.

_____

_____

_____

_____

_____

3. What are some areas of your life that you can afford to freestyle? And what are some areas that you most definitely want to have a "written" for?

Free-style	Written
1) _____	1) _____
2) _____	2) _____
3) _____	3) _____
4) _____	4) _____
5) _____	5) _____

4. Most people at your age/stage of life have had "ghost-writers" or "co-writers" helping them put together their life-verse. Why might it be a good idea to have help with this? **And** who are some of your co/ghost writers?

    _____

    _____

    _____

    _____

5. Just like freestyling rappers use _____ when they run out of things to say, people who freestyle their way through life have things they fall back and lean on when they run out of things to do. What are some _____ that people use in life?

1) _____   6) _____

2) _____   7) _____

3) _____   8) _____

4) _____   9) _____

5) _____   10) _____

6. Sometimes life can throw things at you that will force you to have to freestyle. What are some things that can take a person by surprise and knock him/her off of their written plan?

    1) _____

    2) _____

    3) _____

    4) _____

    5) _____

7. Even if they have good writtens, some rappers develop skills to help them when they're forced to freestyle. What can you develop to help you stay on track when life forces you to freestyle? And how will this help?

    _____

    _____

8. People that leave legacies that we read about years after their accomplishments, do you think they probably freestyled their way through life or had some kind of plan? *And* Can you think of any examples to support your answer?

_____

_____

_____

_____

_____

_____

_____

_____

_____

Outro

Pick at least two areas from question #3 and develop a "written" for them. Get as detail-specific as you can

_____

_____

_____

_____

_____

_____

_____

_____

_____

Preliminary Lesson 4: Character Development

Having a solid plan written for your life is a great start. But it will take more than that to achieve and maintain success. Character Is Key.

Student Learning Outcomes: As a result of this lesson, I can

- Define character
- Explain its importance
- List key character traits that I need to develop in order to reach and retain my goals.

………

Intro

What's the difference between _____ and _____? And which do you think you have more of? **Explain**.

_____

_____

_____

_____

_____

_____

_____

_____

Diving In – Knowledge of Self

1. One way to describe the difference between the two is by saying _____ is *how* you are but _____ is *who* you are.

2. Which of the following personality traits do you possess?

    Circle or check at least three that apply and give an example for them

> * Adventurous
> * Agreeable
> * Independent
> * Charming
> * Outgoing
> * Laidback
> * Humorous
> * Optimistic
> * Hardworking
> * Confident
> * Pleasant
> * Shy
> * Sly
> * Reflective
> * Resourceful

3. Match the following traits with their definitions:

*	**Considerate**	A	You tell the truth, even when it looks bad for you
*	**Honest**	B	People have a good reason to trust you.
*	**Altruistic**	C	You live a life worth imitating
*	**Responsible**	D	You make yourself answerable to others
*	**Accountable**	E	People can count on you to do what is required of you
*	**Consistent**	F	You care about how your life and actions affect other people?
*	**Trust-worthy**	G	People can expect these qualities from you on a regular basis.
*	**Exemplary**	H	Treat self and others in an honorable way
*	**Respectful**	I	Willing to make personal sacrifices for the good of others

4. List 3 of the above traits you believe you possess?

1. _____

2. _____

3. _____

5. Which traits would those who know you best say you need to work on?

1. _____

2. _____

3. _____

6. Which traits would you be okay with your closest friends not possessing?

1. _____

2. _____

3. _____

7. Which traits would you be okay with your boyfriend/girlfriend/future husband/wife not possessing?

1. _____

2. _____

3. _____

8. Even if you have a written plan for your life, what are some things that life can throw at you that will force you to have to "freestyle" and what are some "crutches" people lean on in those situations when they don't have a plan or the character to stick to it?

Life could throw:	Some "Crutches" people lean on are:
1) _____	1) _____
2) _____	2) _____
3) _____	3) _____
4) _____	4) _____
5) _____	5) _____

9. How could developing strong character help you to not fall back on negative "crutches" when life forces you to freestyle? (Do this for two of the situations listed in #9 – choose at least one character trait for each situation)

_____

_____

_____

_____

_____

10. "Talent will take you anywhere, but Character will keep you there" is a popular saying. What do you think this means and can you think of any real-life examples where the opposite of this has happened?

_____

_____

_____

_____

11. Sowing and Reaping: How we get character

Sow a _____ Reap an _____ . Sow an _____ Reap a _____ .

Sow a _____ Reap a _____ . Sow a _____ Reap a _____ .

....

Outro

Identify at least two character traits that you desire? THEN make a list of actions and habits you can begin to sow in order to reap those traits.

Considerate	**I**ntegrity	**K**ind
Honest	**S**elf-control	**E**mpathetic
Altruistic		**Y**ielding
Responsible		
Accountable		
Consistent		
Trustworthy		
Exemplary		
Respectful		

_____

_____

_____

_____

_____

_____

_____

_____

_____

_____

_____

Horncore

Character in Hip Hop

1. What are the top 3 character traits that you think most popular rappers have or that are promoted in rap music?

_____

_____

_____

2. What are the top 3 character traits that you think most popular rappers lack?

_____

_____

_____

3. Why do you think it is not "cool" or "common" to see C.H.A.R.A.C.T.ER. in the Hip Hop community?

_____

_____

_____

Considerate

Honest

Altruistic

Responsible

Accountable

Consistent

Trustworthy

Exemplary

Respectful

Integrity

Self-control

Kind

Empathetic

Yielding

Character in the Media

Directions - Watch the video clip of Lil Wayne's response to questions concerning the Black Lives Matter movement. Then read T.I.'s open letter to him and answer the following questions.

"@liltunechi This is my son & daughter showing me this for the first time & asking me what you mean? I'm at a complete loss of words here. Wayne I've known you over a decade. Our daughters grew up together practically. Reginae' spent countless times at my house with Niq-Niq when you were in prison & you extended my daughter the same courtesy when I was in the same position. Our relationship outside of music is what makes me sensitive to your disposition. I KNOW you're wired a bit different than most other responsible adults, but still n*gga U TRIPPING!!!! I don't know what you goin thru, or what you are attempting to avoid but this sh*t is absolutely unacceptable!!!! You're disrespecting yourself, bringing shame on your family name & tarnishing your legacy. You have children (including mines prior to now) that have looked up to you. You have sons & a daughter that depend upon your leadership. Bro if you don't stand for something out here, all the money, jewelry, cars, mansions bandannas & hit records don't mean sh*t!!!! Our people are being oppressed!!! We are being hunted, captured & slaughtered out here daily!!! You have to get outta that bubble that you've been living in & get out here & educate yourself on what's going on around US!!! I'm always here to share whatever knowledge or understanding I may have to assist your growth & development, but u MUST STOP this buffoonery & coonin' you out here doin. You looking like somebody who has something to gain or lose by pretending like it's not as bad as BLM making it seem & you're not aware of an issue that needs to be addressed. That's what would be considered "Uncle Tom Sh*t".... I know U, YOURE BETTER THAN THIS!!!!! I've been proud to call myself a fan & a friend of Lil Wayne, but if that must end in order to stand up for those who can't do it for themselves...So be it. If you're not prepared for a question in an interview, say No Comment Bro. But stop embarrassing yourself & everyone out here who's been supporting you. There is no middle ground. Oppression knows no neutral party, either you're part of the oppressed, or you with the oppressor. There is no such thing as oppression not affecting you. It's #USorELSE out here"

1) Which character trait(s) is T.I. trying to get Lil Wayne to be more of? Cite a line from this letter for each trait you list.

_____

_____

_____

_____

2) Some say that T.I. should have called Wayne personally instead of posting online. Do you agree? **And WHY** do you think T.I. chose to make a public statement?

_____

_____

_____

3) In the past, Lil Wayne has rapped the following lyrics:

    a. My girl is prego but I don't want it so I'll 'cut it out' like Joey Gladstone

    b. I'm a pill popping' animal, syrup sipping n*gga/ I'm so high you couldn't reach me with a f*ckin antenna

    c. Shoot a n*gga in his thigh and leg and tell him catch up like Mayonnaise

    d. I don't know karate but after the brain I kick you out

    e. And me I'm still spitting like a retard

    f. Kidnap your niece, don't cry, call your uncle / We don't wanna hurt ya baby, we just want your uncle

    g. I beat the p*ssy up like Emmitt Till

Question: Was it responsible of T.I. to let his children listen to Wayne's music before? Or do you think T.I. should have had the same problem with these lyrics that he had with Lil Wayne's BLM statement? **Explain your answer.**

_____

_____

_____

_____

_____

_____

4) Why do you think T.I. had a problem with Wayne's BLM statement but had no problem letting his children look up to Wayne and his music before then?

_____

_____

_____

_____

5) Pick just one word in T.I.'s letter that you think is most important to him and captures everything he is trying to say to Wayne. Explain why you chose that word.

_____

_____

_____

_____

Unit 1
From Hippies to Hip Hop

- Institutional Memory
- Rock & Roll
- Black Power
- Blaxploitation

Overview: Sometimes, in order to move forward, we must first look back to consider how we got to this point. If we want to understand the ethics of Hip Hop culture, we need to know what came before it, both musically and culturally. As it happens, the short period of history between the assassination of Dr. King and the birth of Hip-Hop brought sweeping social changes that paved the way for the new culture.

Student Learning Outcomes: By the end of this unit, you will be able to

- Define 'Institutional Memory' and recognize examples
- Deduce why most African American youth avoided the major "teenager" movement of the 1960's
- Explain what is meant by the term "Cultural Appropriation" and give two examples from history
- Compare and contrast the morality of the Civil Rights Movement, the Black Power Movement and the Blaxploitation film genre/era as it relates to black criminalization.

Lesson 1: Institutional Memory - The Presence of the Past

Institutional Memory is _____

_____

_____

Organizations, Businesses, Buildings, Schools, Family, Street Life (The Block), Prison, Law Enforcement

Examples: _____

_____

_____

Is this a case of Institutional Memory? **Explain** why or why not.

1. A group of teens gather to throw a pair of sneakers up onto the electric wire which runs between the telephone poles along the street where they live. One of the teens asks, 'Why are we doing this, and who started this practice in the first place?" None of them has an answer.

    Yes or No   Explain your choice

    _____

    _____

2. Byron asks his mother for a raise in his allowance. When she asks why he believes he deserves a one, his response is: "When my older brother turned my age you gave him a raise. So, if you don't give me one that's not fair."

    Yes or No   Explain your choice

    _____

    _____

3. As soon as Teishon leaves school at 3:09, he immediately untucks his shirt and adjusts his pants so that they can sag. When Teishon's mother asks him and his friends why they let their pants sag that way, he responds, "Cuz, this is just the way we like it." His mother then asks, "But do you know where that comes from and what it means?" His answer: "Yeah I know, I know . . . you're gonna say prison but, it's just cool." His mother walked away but turned back to ask, "Why are you dressing like you're in prison?"

    Yes or No   Explain your choice

    _____

    _____

4. Martina's mother is teaching her how to roast a Chicken. "The first thing you have to do," her mother tells her, "is cut the chicken in half. Then place one half in a roasting pan and put it on the top rack of the oven; and put the other half on the lower rack." Martina then asked, "Is that so it can cook better?" But her mother responded, "I don't know. That's just the way I've always done it since my mother taught me. Let me call her and find out." So, she called. Martina's grandmother answered the phone and explained, "The only reason I used to cut the bird in half was because our oven wasn't wide enough to fit the whole thing. But your oven is certainly big enough for it to fit without being cut in two."

   Yes   or   No   Explain your choice.

   _____

   _____

5. A white man asks his black friend if she voted for Obama. The woman responds, "Of course! I had to support the brutha." They laugh, but then he then asks, "Do you think most African Americans voted for him because of his ethnicity?" She thinks for a moment and then says, "Yeah, probably." If she is correct in her opinion, would "most African Americans voting for Obama" because of his ethnicity be a case of institutional memory?

   Yes   or   No   Explain your choice.

   _____

   _____

6. A 50-year-old black man in the southern United States puts on a hat and goes out to vote in the presidential election. His 22-year-old son comments, "Dad, how come I never see you wear a hat all year long. But every time you go to vote, you put one on?" The father thinks for a moment and then remembers how his own father used to always wear a hat when voting because, back in the 1960s, blacks thought it was best to disguise themselves in case there were whites waiting to punish them for exercising their right to vote.

   Yes   or   No   Explain your choice.

   _____

   _____

Institutional Memory vs. being Institutionalized

Watch the video clip from the movie *Shawshank Redemption*

Question: What is the difference between **Institutional Memory** and **Institutionalized?**

Your Answer:

_____

_____

Or you could say:

_____

_____

Institutional Memory in the Black Experience

1. Rappers standing around in a circle (cypher) rapping - _____

_____

2. Talking down about one another or each other's mother - _____

_____

3. A very smart 11th grade student makes jokes when the teacher calls on her because she doesn't want to show how intelligent she really is - _____

_____

4. A rapper wants to belittle his opponent, so he brags, "I gotcha baby-mom in the telly waitin'" –

_____

_____

5. Two twelfth graders are making fun of a 10th grader because he doesn't have any name-brand cloths or shoes -

_____

_____

6. Rappers objectifying women and talking about sex in their songs to prove their manhood - _____

_____

Outro

1. Which of the above cases of institutional memory have you personally engaged in? And what do you think about that behavior now, in light of today's lesson? (e.g. Would you continue to do it? Why or why not?)

_____

_____

_____

2. Which of the above cases of institutional memory do you think is the most detrimental to your culture/community? Explain your choice.

_____

_____

_____

3. Choose at least one of the above cases of institutional memory that you want to stop engaging in or supporting. Identify someone in your life who you can trust to hold you accountable to this goal.

_____

_____

Lesson 2: Arrested Development

It is tempting to think that once we reach a certain age, we will be "grown" and have the character we desire. But many people experience **Arrested Development**. This is what it is called when people are stuck in a stage of life that is far behind their age in life.

Student Learning Outcomes: As a result of this lesson, I can

- Explain how America created teen-agers
- Decide if it is ever a good idea to be one

....

Intro

1) By what age is someone definitely an adult?

16   18   21   25   30   other _____

2) What does it mean to "be an adult"?

_____

_____

3) Do you know anyone who is an adult biologically (age-wise) but still lives like a teen? If so, **WHAT** do they still do that is "teen-agerish"?

_____

_____

4) Before 1938, children as young as 7 years old worked on farms and in factories for 12 to 18 hours a day, 6 days a week. Other children chose to go to school. If you had a choice as a child, which would you choose, working full-time or going to school, **AND WHY**?

_____

_____

_____

_____

Diving In - How America Created Teenagers

1) The _____ of 1938 stated that children under 16 yrs old

could no longer _____ during _____ hours and those under 14 could not

even work during _____ hours.

2) The term _____ first appeared in the dictionary in _____.

3) Nouns define things, adjectives describe things. Is the word _____ better seen
as a noun or an adjective? WHY?

_____

3-a) Is the following a <u>description</u> or a <u>definition</u>?

      Black, thin, rectangular, with buttons, voice command, fits in hand, needs battery to work

3-b) What could 5-a be talking about?

_____

6) What does the word "Teenager" tell you about a person?

_____

_____

7) The word does not tell you what a person _____ or _____. It is a

_____ and an _____.

8-a) What are some things that teens CAN do?

_____

8-b) Goodwin's definition of "teenager" is –

_____

9) In other parts of the world, people become "adults" as early as _____ years old.

They become _____ but never become _____.

10) If someone was born in the 1940's or 1950's, how old would they be in 1967? _____-_____

11) The _____ occurred in 1967 and was the biggest _____ gathering until Woodstock in 1969.

12) Which of the following were values of the Hippie movement?

Rejection of authority	Desire for Material things/money	Peace and Unity
Rejection of Material/Money	Respect for Parents Beliefs	Fight for the American way
Anti-drug	Heavy Psychedelic drug use	Heavy Marijuana use
Rejection of traditional fashion	Desire to take part in capitalism/commercialism	Free Love

Lesson 3: Sex, Drugs and Rock & Roll

It is no secret that much of popular white culture has been "borrowed" from black culture over the last two centuries. But there are some things that, perhaps, blacks may not want to take credit for – things that, in their original, cultural context did not have quite the same meaning as when they ended up in white hands.

Student Learning Outcomes: As a result of this lesson, I can

- Explain what is meant by "cultural appropriation"
- Identify at least three key figures from the genres of Blues and Rock & Roll
- Contrast the values of Rock & Roll with those of Rock music.

....

Intro

1. Many white youth who were "teen-agers" in the 1950's became _____ in the 60's
   a. Educated
   b. Responsible
   c. Examples
   d. Hippies

2. Pick two words from the box that you think best describe the way black youth in the 1960's felt when they saw white youth becoming "hippies".

Relieved	Upset	Jealous
Confused	Excited	Disappointed
Amused	Thrilled	Worried/ Scared

3. Explain why you chose the two words you selected in # 1

1st Word _____

_____

2nd Word _____

_____

4. If the hippies' 1967 Summer of Love had never happened before but was scheduled to happen this coming summer, what rappers do you think would fit right in with their "teen-ager" life-style *AND* what rappers do you think would not participate?

Would be down with it   **Would _not_ be down with it**

_____   _____

_____   _____

_____   _____

_____   _____

5. What character traits would someone need to possess if he/she wanted to resist the urge to celebrate the Summer of Love? **And how** would those traits help? (Pick two)

1. _____

   _____

2. _____

   _____

Diving In - Cultural Appropriation

1. Why do you think the "hippies" were mostly white? Why did most young blacks not participate in the major "teen-ager" movement of the 1960's?

_____

_____

_____

2. The Hippies were seen as 'cultural rebels.' One of the ways white youth rebelled was by gravitating towards

_____ such as _____ which was originally called

_____.

3. Originally, blues musicians like _____ & _____ used the term

_____ as a *euphemism* for _____, just like the term _____.

4. The 1ˢᵗ recorded _____ song was in _____ by _____ &

_____.

5. Why do you think black young-adults sung about sex before and during the 1950's?

      a) Because they were still "teen-agers"
      b) Because they wanted to seem more like grown men and women
      c) Because they had no morals
      d) Because it's just a natural part of life

6. Why do you think white young-adults started singing about sex during the 1950's?

      a) Because they were still "teen-agers"
      b) Because they wanted to seem more like grown men and women
      c) Because they had no morals
      d) Because it's just a natural part of life

7. Do you think it is immoral to focus on sex without, at the same time, focusing on marriage?

     Yes or No: Explain as an

      Egoist _____

      Utilitarian _____

      Deontological _____

8. In the 1960's, it was difficult for black men to affirm their manhood in the eyes of society. Singing about sexually pleasing women was a way to do accomplish this. But was that the only way? What are some others?

_____

_____

9. Back in the 1950's, two radio DJs helped Rock & Roll become a part of *pop-culture*. _____ did it in Cleveland by _____ the music of black artists on air. But _____ in Philadelphia did it by playing white artists who _____ black music.

10. The Beatles, a British band whose music invaded the U.S. in a major way in the 1960's, were heavily influenced by African American, Rock & Rollers _____ and _____. Another British group, The Rolling Stones, were greatly influenced by blues legends _____ and _____. But the white artist who rose to the highest fame by covering Rock & Roll was _____ AKA _____.

Outro

1. Listen to the 1998 song "Rock & Roll" by Mos Def. Choose 1 – 3 words/phrases from the song that explains the way he feels about the history of Rock & Roll? **Explain** why you chose those words.

   (1) _____

   _____

   (2) _____

   _____

   (3) _____

   _____

2. Do you think the same thing that happen to Rock & Roll could ever happen to Hip Hop and how would you feel if it did?

   _____

   _____

   _____

3. Is this line from the popular rapper _____ acceptable? Why or why not?

   _____

   _____

   _____

Lesson 4: Movements on the Way to Hip Hop

Before we look further at the musical shifts which led to Hip Hop, we need to understand what was happening in society around the time Hip Hop was born. This will explain why rap sometimes sounds more like the makings of a movement and not just like people making music.

Student Learning Outcomes: As a result of this lesson, I can

- Name and differentiate between the two movements that predated Hip Hop.

....

Intro

1. What did Dr. Martin Luther King think about Hip Hop music?

      a. It was too violent for him
      b. It could be used but only if done a certain way
      c. He had no thoughts on the subject
      d. It wasn't "real" music like Rock & Roll and Soul music

2. What did Malcolm X think about Hip Hop music?

      a. He wanted it to be more militant
      b. As a Muslim, he didn't think rap or any music with instruments was acceptable
      c. He had no thoughts on the subject
      d. It wasn't "real" music like Rock & Roll and Soul music

3. Based on what you know about these two men, name 3 rappers of today that you think Dr. King would have approved of, and 3 that you think Malcolm X would have approved of.

<table>
<tr><td align="center">Martin</td><td align="center">Malcolm</td></tr>
<tr><td>_____

_____

_____</td><td>_____

_____

_____</td></tr>
</table>

Diving In – Move Sumthin'

1. Most African Americans were fans of Dr. Martin Luther King and the Civil Rights Movement before he was assassinated.

       True   OR   False

2. Dr. King was taken from the world 5 years before Hip Hop came on the scene. What years did these two events occur?

        a. 1970 and 1975

        b. 1963 and 1968

        c. 1966 and 1971

        d. 1968 and 1973

3. Around 1964, another movement began to grow in popularity. It was the _____ Movement.

        a. Black Panther

        b. Black Spades

        c. Black Power

        d. Black Lives Matter

        e. Wakanda Forever

4. Which of the following Malcolm X speech titles goes best with his famous motto "By Any Means Necessary"? **Explain** how the title you chose matches the motto.

        a. A Declaration of Independence

        b. The Ballot or the Bullet

        c. A Message to the Grassroots

        d. The Black Revolution

_____

_____

_____

5. In the late 1960's, especially after the death of King, many young blacks got involved in the

_____ movement. But others got involved in street-life and

_____.

6. What are some similarities and differences between a movement and a _____?

Similarities   **Differences**

_____	_____
_____	_____
_____	_____
_____	_____

7. Black Panther Party founder Huey P. Newton wanted to take young blacks off the corners and get them _____ and _____; this is what was known as _____.

     a. Armed and Dangerous; Woke

     b. Trained and Ready; A Militia

     c. Educated and Politically Organized; Conscious

9. After the death of Dr. King, many young blacks remembered the words of Malcolm X and felt it was time to choose the _____ and no longer the _____. Spoken-word artists such as _____ and The _____ began to call for _____.

10. If you were alive at the time, would you have been a part of either movement? And if so, which one and why?

_____

_____

_____

_____

_____

_____

Outro

Listen to the 1970 poetic work *The Revolution Will Not be Televised* by Gil Scott Heron and the 1970 poetic work *N*ggers are Scared of Revolution* by the Last Poets, then answer at least 3 of the following questions:

1. Why might blacks have been scared of "revolution"?

_____

_____

_____

2. What is the difference between revolution and evolution and when it comes to social change, which do you think would be best for our society today? **Explain**

_____

_____

_____

_____

_____

_____

_____

_____

_____

_____

_____

_____

_____

Lesson 5: Stopping the Movements

Not only was there an inhouse debate amongst black Americans about which of the two movements was more moral at the time; there was also outside interference from the highest office in the land which targeted both movements.

Student Learning Outcomes: As a result of this lesson, I can

- Explain Black Criminalization
- State the lasting impact of the War on Drugs

....

Intro

1. What is a stereotype? _____

2. What do you think is the most harmful stereotype about black men

    a. They're Lazy

    b. They're after white women

    c. They're more likely to be Criminals

    d. They are all good at basketball

3. Explain your choice for #2 (why is it the most harmful?)

_____

_____

_____

_____

_____

Diving In – Hold Up…Wait A Minute!

Directions: Use the words in the box to begin answering the questions below.

Ice T	Tupac	Blacks & Hippies	Law & Order
45	Richard Nixon	Ronald Reagan	Peace & Prosperity
War on Drugs	Blacks & Latinos	25	Mandatory Minimum
50%	An End to War	90%	Guilty

1. In 1968, _____ began to campaign for President of the United States on the promise of returning America to a state of _____.

2. This coded language referred to which two "dis-orderly" groups of people?
   _____

3. After promising a war on Crime, in 1971, President Nixon declared _____.

4. Twenty years later, _____ said that the "The War on Drugs is a war on you and me." What do you think he meant by this?

   _____

   _____

   _____

5. Today, harsh _____ sentencing forces _____ percent of defendants to plead _____ instead of going to trial to fight their case.[1]

6. What are the benefits (**B**) of and drawbacks (**DR**) of taking a plea bargain?

Lesser Charges __	Definite Conviction __	Reduced Sentence __
Giving up Right to Trial __	Costs the Tax-Payers Less __	Criminal Record __
Save Lawyers and Judges Time __	Social Privileges Revoked __	No Standing before Judge __

---

[1] http://www.uscourts.gov/about-federal-courts/types-cases/criminal-cases (7/23/2018)

7. Which of the following is the worst result of the War on Drugs? **Explain** why

   a. It took many black men away from their families and placed them in jail/prison
   b. Many African Americans lost their right to vote after being convicted of felonies
   c. It penalized people for simply trying to meet their basic needs.

   _____

   _____

   _____

8. The War on Drugs has lasted just over _____ years.

9. At the end of his last term in office, President Barack Obama began to put an end to the War on Drugs. Why do you think he waited until the end of his presidency?

   _____

   _____

   _____

10. In the first couple of months of his first year in office, President Donald Trump and his Attorney General, Jeff Sessions _____ many of President Obama policies aimed at ending the War on Drugs. Is "racism" the only possible explanation for this? Or could there be another reason? **Explain**

   _____

   _____

   _____

Outro

Watch the video for the 1989 song "Fight the Power" by Public Enemy then answer the following questions.

1) According to this artist, what is the difference between his music and his lyrics?

_____

_____

2) According to this artist, art comes from the heart. What does his art tell you about his heart?

_____

_____

3) What does the music of your favorite rapper tell you about his/her heart?

_____

_____

4) Based on the "Fight the Power" lyrics, why are some black people "not the same" as others?

_____

_____

5) Chuck D was a fan of Dr. Martin Luther King and his methods.

   True   OR   False

Lesson 6: Blaxploitation Pt 1

The same year that President Nixon declared the War on "Drugs" that painted black people as criminals, something else was born; a film genre that had the potential to improve the image of African Americans in the media and in the eyes of the country. As positive as this sounds, this new genre immediately came to be known as "Blaxploitation"—a negative term.

Student Learning Outcomes: As a result of this lesson, I can

- Name and contrast at least two black entertainers from before the Blaxploitation era
- Explain why the film genre that came to be known as Blaxploitation was so refreshing at first

…………………………………………………………………………………………………

Intro

Read and Answer:

It's Halloween and you're home waiting to give out candy to trick-or-treaters. Someone rings your doorbell. As you open the door, you see five or six people who look to be in their late teens or early 20's, dressed like King T'Challa and the Dora Majale from the Black Panther movie. As you look closer, you realize that everyone in the group is white. They are not wearing masks but have painted their skin dark brown as part of their costume.

1. What do you do?

   a. Start cursing and swinging
   b. Educate them on why they have made a poor choice
   c. Compliment them for choosing a great costume and characters to portray
   d. Slam the door, then open it again to take a picture of them to post online

   Explain your choice

_____

_____

_____

Diving In – Color Me Badd

1. In the 1800s and early 1900s, the first black people who were seen performing in the entertainment industry were actually white people.

   True   OR   False

2. In those days, _____ performances were very common. Why do you think that was the case?

   _____

   _____

3. What is one positive (P) and one negative (N) aspect of whites doing this kind of art?

   P_____

   N_____

4. The most **infamous** case of _____ performance was in the 1915, silent film

   _____.

5. Before and even after that outrageous film, some black entertainers also performed in blackface.
   True   OR   False

6. _____, the highest paid African American stage performer in the 1910's, said that he "found himself" when he put on _____ for the first time. What do you think he could have meant by this?

   _____

   _____

7. An African American actor named Lincoln Perry created a character that made him famous. He appeared in over forty films between 1927 and 1939 and was the first black actor to become a millionaire. He did this by, over and over again, playing the role of _____, aka "the laziest man in the world."

   a. Would you have played this role over and over again in the 1930's if you knew it would make you a millionaire? Why or Why not?

   _____

   _____

b. Lincoln Perry did not use blackface paint, but how could his character 'Stepin Fetchit' still be compared to that style of art?

_____

_____

_____

_____

8. The first black woman to win an Academy Award was _____, for _____ in _____.

   a. Hattie McDaniel for *Gone with the Wind* in 1939

   b. Josephine Baker for *Princess Tam Tam* in 1935

   c. Holly Berry for *Monster's Ball* in 2002

   d. Beyoncè for *Dream Girls* in 2006

9. The first black man to win an Academy Award was _____, for _____ in _____.

   a. Bert Williams for The Railroad Porter in 1913

   b. Lincoln Perry for *Miracle in Harlem* in 1948

   c. Sidney Portier for Lilies of the Field in 1964

   d. Denzel Washington for *Training Day* in 2001

10. The week after Martin Luther King was assassinated, _____ won the Academy Award for best actor in the film _____.

11. Using character traits and vices, how could you compare the careers of Lincoln Perry and Sidney Portier?

_____

_____

_____

Outro

1. Before the 1970s, blacks were mainly portrayed as _____ in movies.

        a. Immoral Criminals
        b. Happy Servants
        c. Sad Slaves

2. If blacks could only play one role in Hollywood films, which of the above roles (a, b or c) would be best and which worst? **Explain** your answer.

_____

_____

_____

_____

_____

3. If a new film genre that African Americans could be excited about came on the scene in 1971, what would you expect some of the differences to be between the new genre and the way Hollywood treated blacks before that time? (try to use the character traits and the vices in your answer)

_____

_____

_____

_____

_____

_____

_____

_____

_____

_____

Lesson 7: Blaxploitation Pt 2

In 1971, thanks to the War on Drugs, blacks were being **vilified** on the evening news and harassed by police in their neighborhoods. Dr. King had been assassinated and the Black Power Movement was trying to spark a revolution. The old Hollywood portrayal of blacks as quiet servants was now unbelievable and unsustainable. So, a new genre of film aimed to capture the defiant black spirit of that time.

Student Learning Outcomes: As a result of this lesson, I can

- Define Blaxploitation
- Explain in what ways it helped and in what ways it held back African American advancement in the 1970's

....

Intro

Listen to the 1971 song "Inner City Blues" by Marvin Gaye

1. List three things from the song that you believe are still happening in society today.

   _____

   _____

   _____

2. List three things from the song that you believe you have personally experienced.

   _____

   _____

   _____

3. How does it make you feel that the things Marvin sung about in 1971 are still happening today?

   _____

   _____

   _____

4. Do you think the things you listed above (#'s 1 and 2) will still be happening when your children are your age? **And**, what can you do to make sure they are not still occurring?

   _____

Diving In – New Directors, New Directions

1. Before the 1970's, old Hollywood struggled to depict blacks co-existing in
   _____, but Blaxploitation films sought to bring the camera into
   _____.

2. The first film in this genre was _____, which was
   a. Written and produced by African Americans
   b. Written, produced and directed by African Americans
   c. Written, produced, directed and starred by African Americans
   d. Written, produced, directed and starred by the same African American man

3. The film showed a young black man who dared to stand up to the _____ in his neighborhood
   and the whole _____ came together to protect him. By the end he became conscious.
   a. Gangs; Police force
   b. Drug-dealers; City council
   c. Police; Community

4. What did the **Black Panther Party** co-founder **Huey P. Newton** do when he saw the film?
   a. He made it mandatory for every Black Panther member nationwide to see it
   b. Dedicated a whole issue of the Party's magazine to analyzing and praising the film
   c. Helped sell tickets for the film which made it a huge success
   d. Told the Panthers not to go see it but to make their own "black power" movies instead
   e. A, B and C

5. What made the movie attractive to Black Power types was
   a. The main character fought against police brutality
   b. The whole community, even the pimps and hustlers helped the main character evade police
   c. The movie was the first to depict Black Power characters
   d. All of the above
   e. A and C

6. Throughout the 1970's, as more films were written and produced by and starred African Americans
   a. The movies and messages in the genre became even more conscious
   b. More and more whites began to write the movies
   c. The movies began to celebrate black pimps, prostitutes and drug-dealers
   d. A & C
   e. B & C

7. If "B & C" from #6 were combined, how could that be compared to _____
   performances?

   _____

   _____

   _____

8. If "A & C" from #6 were combined, how could that be compared to the _____ performances of Burt Williams? (Remember what else was going on in the 1970s)

_____

_____

_____

9. Would combining "A & C" have been a good/moral way to address the problems of the 70's? Why or why not? What character traits come to mind when answering this question?

_____

_____

_____

_____

_____

_____

10. In what ways were Blaxploitation films different from the films of old Hollywood and helpful to the advancement of African Americans and in what ways, not so different?

_____

_____

_____

_____

Outro

Which was better, and which would you choose if you were an African American actor/actress who really wanted to work in Hollywood: old Hollywood in the early 1900's when blacks could get many small roles by **only** playing maids, butlers and chauffeurs OR the 1970's when blacks could get lead roles but **had to** play Pushers, Pimps and Prostitutes? **Explain** your answer?

_____

_____

_____

_____

_____

_____

_____

_____

_____

_____

_____

_____

_____

_____

_____

_____

_____

_____

_____

Unit 2
The Origins of Hip-Hop

- The Birth of Hip Hop
- The Stages of Rap

A lot happened in the six years between the birth of the Hippies and the birth of Hip-Hop. With that history in mind, we will begin to connect the dots between the past and the present since we are now in a better position to understand the moral trajectory of rap music in its various forms.

Student Learning Outcomes: By the end of this unit, you will be able to

- Explain how the past can impact the present on a subconscious level
- Recite the story of Hip-Hop's origin including important dates, names and events
- Differentiate between at least three different "stages" of rap

Lesson #1: Hip Hop's Institutional Memory

You've probably heard the saying, "Two wrongs don't make a right." And yet, when it comes to rap music, many artists sound like they think they have a right to be wrong. Have you ever wondered where this sense of moral entitlement comes from?

> **Student Learning Outcomes**: As a result of this lesson, I can
> - Trace the two historical roots of Hip-Hop culture's ethics
> - Decide which of those two influences I will support going forward

....

Intro

1. Which do you think had the greater influence upon the young adults who gave birth to Hip Hop culture: The Black Power Movement or the Blaxploitation film genre? **Explain**

Answer: I think the first Hip Hoppers took more from _____. I say that because _____

_____.

2. Which one would it been better for Hip Hop to take after? **Explain** briefly

_____

_____

_____

3. Name 3 rappers that take after Black Power more and 3 that take after Blaxploitation more

Black Power	**Blaxploitation**
_____	_____
_____	_____
_____	_____

Old School Rap, Mix & Match: Match the following artists to their album titles

Snoop Dogg

                             Back for the First Time

50 Cent

                             Bigger & Deffer

L.L. Cool J

                             Brother, Can I Borrow a Dollar?

Luda Cris

                             Black on Both Sides

Ice T

                             God's Son

Common

                             Country Grammar

Flavor Flav

                             The Massacre

Queen Latifa

                             Black Reign

Ice Cube

                             Fear of a Black Planet

Nelle

                             Power

Nas

                             The Last Meal

Most Def

                             Predator

Listen to the song "No Romeo" by 50 Cent then answer the following questions.

1. 50 Cent brags about "pimping" women, do you think this is something to be proud of? Why or why not?

_____

_____

_____

2. List 3 words to describe how you would feel if you heard a man talking to a woman the same way 50 does in verse 1?

_____

_____

_____

3. In what decade did "pimping" become cool?

    a. 1950's

    b. 1960's

    c. 1970's

    d. 1980's

4. Which old-school rapper(s) got his name, game or fame from something related to a Pimp or pimping?

    a. Big Daddy Kane

    b. Ice T.

    c. Too $hort

    d. Trick Daddy

5. Kool G. Rap says that in the 1980's, his friend and fellow Juice Crew member Big Daddy Kane didn't watch the new movies that came out because he was still watching the movies _____ and _____ from the 1970's

a. In the Heat of the Night and Guess Who's Coming to Dinner
b. Star Wars and Star Trek
c. Shaft and Dolemite

6. At the beginning of his "Original Gangsta" album, _____ described himself as "the epitome of antidisestablishmentarianism, who embodies the entire spectrum of the urban experience," or, in other words, "the dopest, flyest, OG, pimp, hustler, gangster, player, hardcore, mother-f*cker living today."

Is that statement an example of Black Power or Blaxploitation? _____

Listen to the 2015 song "Mortal Man" by Kendrick Lamar

1. In this song, Kendrick Lamar seems to be asking his fans to be more than fans; what do you think he is asking his fans to become? And what lyrics help you to answer this question?

   _____

   _____

   _____

2. What do you think Kendrick means by the line, "Would you know where the sermon is if I died in this next line"?

   _____

   _____

   _____

3. Look back at the beginning of this lesson. Do any of the words you used to describe what Hip Hop gets from the Black Power Movement fit this song? If so, which ones? Do any of the words you used to describe what Hip Hop gets from the Blaxploitation era fit this song? If so, which ones?

   _____

   _____

   _____

Outro

Consider the playlists in your phone (or wherever your music is stored).

1. List at least three rap artists in your playlists that are more one or the other

     Black Power   **Blaxploitation**

     _____   _____

     _____   _____

     _____   _____

2. What percentage of the rap songs in your playlists fits more in one category or the other

     _____% Black Power   _____% Blaxploitation

3. Consider the way Blaxploitation art impacted someone like Big Daddy Kane. Then think about your answer to #2. Are you happy with that ratio or would you like to change it? If so, what would you desire the numbers to be instead?

     _____% Black Power   _____% Blaxploitation

4. What do you think the benefit would be of making this change?

     _____

     _____

5. Who are some artists you can add to make those numbers more like you desire them to be?

     _____

     _____

     _____

Lesson 2: The Birth of Hip Hop

"You love to hear the story, again and again of how it all started way back when." That is the opening line of "The Bridge," a 1986 rap song about Hip-Hop's history and Queens NY.[2] The stories of Hip-Hop's origins are so important because when it began, it was immediately seen as more than just art; it was a sign that there was life beneath the rubble of a devastated city borough.

Student Learning Outcomes: As a result of this lesson, I can

- List at least three facts about the conditions of life in New York City around the time when Hip Hop was born.
- Describe how those conditions contributed to the social significance of Hip Hop

....

Intro

Directions: See if you can fill in the blanks with the words below.

Hip Hop is a _____ that began as a _____. People thought it was going to be a _____ but it has spanned two _____. From the beginning it always had the potential to become a _____.

        a. Generations

        b. Music Style

        c. Fad

        d. Culture

        e. Movement

---

[2] MC Shan, *The Bridge*; 1986

Diving In - Inner City Blues

1. Hip Hop started in _____ .
   a. Queens Bridge, NY in 1986
   b. Harlem, NY in 1970
   c. The Bronx, NY in 1973
   d. Brooklyn, NY in 1980

2. Which of the following things was NOT happening during the decade when Hip-Hop began?
   a. 1,000,000 people, mostly middle-class tax-payers moved away from the city
   b. The city was seconds away from declaring bankruptcy
   c. Black and Latino neighborhoods were constantly on fire and left to burn down
   d. The police force was investigated for wide-spread corruption
   e. A highway was built in the middle of the borough and people were displaced

3. Hip-Hop was born 5 years after what historic event? _____

4. In the 5 years between _____ and the birth of Hip Hop, many young
   blacks in American cities got involved in _____ but some others
   got involved in _____ .

5. Why do you think that is?
   _____
   _____

6. Are there any similarities between a _____ and a _____? If so, what are
   some?

   _____   _____

7. When Hip Hop began, gang activity in New York City stopped almost overnight.
   True or False

8. One man told all the gangs in New York City to stop the violence and become a part of the Hip
   Hop movement. His name was Afrika Bambaataa.   True   or   False

9. Afrika Bambaataa started the _____ and then the _____
   _____ after taking a trip to _____ .

10. Around the same time, Dj _____ introduced the _____ style of
    Dj-ing.

Outro

1. Look back at #2 on the previous page. Which one of those factors do you think had the biggest social/psychological impact on the young adults who invented Hip Hop culture? And which one do you think had the least? Explain your answer.

_____

_____

_____

_____

2. Look back at #2 on the previous page. Using Maslow's Hierarchy, how would you respond to someone who says, "You can't eat morals and character. Growing up in a situation like that, you've gotta do what you gotta do to survive...even if it's immoral. Character can come later."

_____

_____

_____

_____

Lesson 3: The Originators

Fortunately, Hip Hop culture is old enough to have a history but also young enough that many of its originators are still around to tell the story of how it all began. It is a true underdog story that you would never have guessed if you look at today's shiny examples of rappers "balling out of control." By reviewing this history, we can see how much (and how little, in some ways) the culture has changed.

Student Learn Outcomes: As a result of this lesson, I can

- Name three important figures from the early days of Hip-Hop along with their contributions to the culture
- List two things that separated Hip Hop from the musical style that came directly before it

....

Intro

Answer the following question

If rap music and Hip-Hop culture had never been created, how would the world be any different? (e.g. in what ways would things be better? In what ways would things be worse? Are there any historical events in America that would not have occurred if Hip Hop had never existed? And what would be different about your own life?)

_____

_____

_____

_____

_____

_____

_____

_____

Diving In - Reliable Sources

Video response. Watch *Hip Hop Evolution*: Season 1, Episode 1 and answer the following questions.

1) What music style was most popular just before Hip Hop was born?

   _____

2) Who threw Hip Hop's first party?

   _____

3) What year was the first Hip Hop party thrown?

   _____

4) What was significant about the way the first Hip Hop DJ played records?

   _____

5) How did "break dancers" get their name?

   _____

6) What was the vision for the Universal Zulu Nation?

   _____

7) According to Afrika Bambaataa, what is the 5th element of Hip Hop?

   _____

8) What did Grandmaster Flash contribute to Hip Hop's development?

   _____

9) Who was the "Holy Trinity" in Hip Hop?

   _____

10) What are some things that separated Hip Hop from Disco?

   _____

   _____

Lesson 4: Up from the Underground

Just because someone plants a thing in the ground doesn't mean that life will grow from it. The conditions must be right, and the thing planted must be a seed full of the potential for life. In the 1970's the social conditions were just right for change, and the seeds of Hip-Hop would not remain underground.

Student Learning Outcomes: As a result of this lesson, I can
- Name the five "seeds" or elements of Hip-Hop
- Compare, contrast and estimate the impact of two songs that helped bring rap music into the mainstream.

....

Intro

1. Do you think rappers have a responsibility to put out positive messages in their music or do they have the right to make whatever kind of songs they want, even if they are immoral? **Explain**.

   _____

   _____

   _____

2. Some rappers have long careers, lasting over twenty years; others have short careers, lasting less than five. Are there any current rap artists from your generation that you could see still making relevant music 20 years from now. List at least 3

   _____

   _____

   _____

3. Are the artists in your list more in line with Black Power or Blaxploitation?

   _____

4. Do you think there is any connection between your answers to question #1 and #3? **Explain**

   _____

   _____

Diving In - Elements and Compounds

1. Afrika Bambaataa added a 5th element which was _____. But what were the original "Four Elements of Hip Hop"?

    1. _____   2. _____

    3. _____   4. _____

2. The art of rapping is often referred to as "_____" because the very first rappers in Hip-Hop were the _____, or the _____ who _____.

3. Of the four original elements of Hip Hop, which do you think was the most popular, at first? And why?
   _____

4. Very soon, _____ became the most popular element. Why do you think that is?
   _____

   _____

5. The first professionally recorded rap record was _____ in _____. Over time, the single sold more than 14 million copies, but at its peak, it was selling over _____ copies per day.

   a. My Adidas in 1980….1,000,000
   b. Roxanne's Revenge in 1977….10,000
   c. The Breaks in 1979….100,000
   d. Rappers Delight in 1979….50,000

6. The second commercially successful rap song was _____ in _____.
   It went _____ in 11 days and _____ not long after that.

7. What are some similarities and difference between the two songs (name at least 2 of each)

    Similarities   **Differences**

    _____   _____

    _____   _____

    _____   _____

8. Why do you think the 1982 song sold so quickly?

9. The values given to Hip Hop (via the Zulu Nation) from Afrika Bambaataa were

   _____, _____, _____ and <u>having fun</u>, as long as you

   weren't hurting anyone.

   a. Which of these four values would the song "Rapper's Delight" fit under?

      _____

   b. Which of these four values would the song "The Message" fit under?

      _____

10. Which rapper said that when he heard "The Message" at 9 years old in 1982, he felt like he was
    listening to a prophet and it influenced his later rap career and life.

    a. Biggie
    b. Tupac
    c. Nas
    d. Kendric Lamar

Outro

1. Think about the rap songs in your playlist. What percentage would you say are more like "The Message" and what percentage are more like "Rapper's Delight"?

   About _____% are like the "The Message" and about _____% are like "Rapper's Delight"

2. Do you think it's possible for a rap song to be like both of these songs at the same time, having a deep message that you can dance and party to?

   YES   OR   NO

3. If you said "yes" to #2, can you name any songs like this? If you say "no" why not?

   _____

   _____

   _____

   _____

Lesson 5: Stages of Rap Pt. 1

Rappers use their platforms for a variety of reasons. Some make you dance, other make you think. Some switch it up while others are consistant. We can call the platorms of these rappers "categories" or **Stages**.

Student Learning Outcomes: As a result of this lesson, I can
- Identify and list the unique traits of two different stages of rap.

....

Intro

1. If you were watching a movie, what would you think or how would you feel if every time there was a violent shoot-out or a car-chase with loud, explosive crashes, the background music was a soft, sweet, romantic love-song? And everytime there was an intimate love-scene with two people slowly becoming close, the background music was nothing but raukus heavy-metal and rock music?

_____

_____

_____

2. Think about the music that you listen to most often, not just the style but the words. Whatever it is, is that music a fitting soundtrack for your life? i.e. does it match the way you live/want to live? (**Give examples** to support your answer)

_____

_____

_____

_____

_____

Diving In - Stages and Phrases

1. The first stage of rap could be called the _____ stage. Here rappers are talking about _____ and talking to _____.

Talking About	Talking To
• Their Opponents Lack of Skill • Their Own Skills on the Mic • The DJ • Having nice objects • Bringing Cultural/Social Awareness • Keeping the Crowd Hype • Bringing Cultural/Social Destruction • Having Fun • Reinforcing Positive Black Identity • Women as Objects • Reinforcing Negative Black Identity	• Potential Fans • Party Goers • Potential Music Buyers • Other Rappers • America • Black-America Specifically

2. On the _____ stage, rappers are talking about _____, and they are talking to _____.

Talking About	Talking To
• Their Opponents Lack of Skill • Their Own Skills on the Mic • The DJ • Having nice objects • Bringing Cultural/Social Awareness • Keeping the Crowd Hype • Bringing Cultural/Social Destruction • Having Fun • Reinforcing Positive Black Identity • Women as Objects • Reinforcing Negative Black Identity	• Potential Fans • Party Goers • Potential Music Buyers • Other Rappers • America • Black-America Specifically

3. Who changed battle-rap? What did it change from and what did it change to?

    _____

    _____

Identifying the Stages – Find four lines from each song and tell what stage they are on.

1. Listen to "Cha, Cha, Cha" by MC Lyte – 1989 (1st two verses)

Which Stages? / Cite Lyrics to support
1st _____ / _____
2nd _____ / _____
3rd _____ / _____
4th _____ / _____

2. Listen to "Long Live the Kane" by Big Daddy Kane – 1988 (1st verse)

Which Stages? / Cite Lyrics to support
1st _____ / _____
2nd _____ / _____
3rd _____ / _____
4th _____ / _____

Outro

1. What were the values Afrika Bambaataa tried to instill in Hip Hop culture?

    Bambaataa suggested _____, _____, _____ and having _____.

2. Which of those values do you think each stage we discussed so far would fit under? **Explain** how.

    a. The *Party* stage would fit under _____

    _____

    _____

    b. The *Battle* stage would fit under _____

    _____

    _____

3. Do you think the shift in battle-rap was a good/moral addition to the culture or a negative addition? Explain.

    _____

    _____

    _____

    _____

Lesson 6: Stages and Phrases Part 2

1. On the _____ stage, rappers are talking about _____ and
   talking to _____.

Talking About	Talking To
• Their Opponents Lack of Skill • Their Own Skills on the Mic • The DJ • Having nice objects • Bringing Cultural/Social Awareness • Keeping the Crowd Hype • Bringing Cultural/Social Destruction • Having Fun • Reinforcing Positive Black Identity • Women as Objects • Reinforcing Negative Black Identity	• Potential Fans • Party Goers • Potential Music Buyers • Other Rappers • America • Black-America Specifically

    a. Listen to "Rapper's Delight" by The Sugar Hill Gang – 1979 (1st and 2nd verses)

Which Stages? / Cite Lyrics to support

1st _____ / _____

2nd _____ / _____

3rd _____ / _____

4th _____ / _____

    b. Listen to "I Got it Made" by Special Ed – 1989 (2nd and 3rd verses)

Which Stages? / Cite Lyrics to support

1st _____ / _____

2nd _____ / _____

3rd _____ / _____

4th _____ / _____

2. On the _____ stage, rappers are talking about _____ and
   talking to _____ .

Talking About
• Their Opponents Lack of Skill
• Their Own Skills on the Mic
• The DJ
• Having nice objects
• Bringing Cultural/Social Awareness
• Keeping the Crowd Hype
• Bringing Cultural/Social Destruction
• Having Fun
• Reinforcing Positive Black Identity
• Women as Objects
• Reinforcing Negative Black Identity
•

Talking To
• Potential Fans
• Party Goers
• Potential Music Buyers
• Other Rappers
• America
• Black-America Specifically

a. Listen to "Black I'm Proud" by Intelligent Hoodlum – 1990 (1st verse)

Which Stages? / Cite Lyrics to support

1st _____ / _____

2nd _____ / _____

3rd _____ / _____

4th _____ / _____

b. Listen to "My Philosophy" by KRS-ONE – 1988 (2nd verse)

Which Stages? / Cite Lyrics to support

1st _____ / _____

2nd _____ / _____

3rd _____ / _____

4th _____ / _____

The Conscious rap stage can be divided into three time-frames.

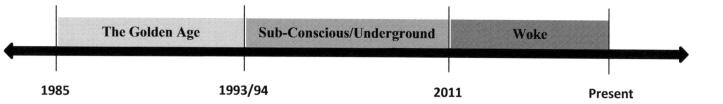

The Golden Age	Sub-Conscious/Underground	Woke

1985   1993/94   2011   Present

1. How many Conscious rappers from the Golden Age of Hip Hop can you name?

   1. _____   5. _____

   2. _____   6. _____

   3. _____   7. _____

   4. _____   8. _____

2. Which ethical system do you think most Conscious rappers subscribed to during the Golden Age?

   a. Ethical Egoism
   b. Utilitarianism
   c. Deontological Ethics

3. Of the four stages or rap mentioned so far, which ones do you think go together very well and which ones do you think would not fit together so well. **Explain**.

   _____

   _____

   _____

   _____

Outro

Of the four stages you learned so far, can you see any influence of the Blaxplotation film era or the Black Power Movement? Explain your answer.

Blaxploitation

_____

_____

_____

_____

Black Power

_____

_____

_____

_____

Lesson 7: Contours of Consciousness

One of the things that made the Golden Age of Hip-Hop so golden was the consciousness within the culture. Because it was such an important feature, we must take a closer look at where this consciousness came from and how it contributed to the ethics of Hip Hop.

Student Learning Outcomes: As a result of this lesson, I can
- List two things that made Conscious rap such a strong force
- Name one thing that kept it from becoming even stronger

....

Intro

1. In your own words, what do you think it means to be "woke"?

_____

_____

_____

2. Are you a "woke" individual? What makes you say 'yes' or 'no'?

_____

_____

_____

Diving In - A Culture of Consciousness

1. One of the most popular Conscious rap groups from the Golden Age was _____ which consisted of Flavor Flav and _____.

(a) Chuck Berry   (b) Chuck Chill-out   (c) Chucky from Child's Play   (d) Chuck D

2. What did _____ wear around his neck and why did he wear it?

   _____

3. What was Flavor Flav's role in the group?

(a) Hype-man   (b) Comic Relief   (c) Best Rapper   (d) Mascott

4. We can also see his role as painting a _____ or _____

   _____ picture.

5. The Deontological world-view of most Conscious rappers during the Golden Age was that of

   a. 5 Percenters who believed that the black man is god
   b. Christians who believed that sins could only be paid for by Jesus' death on the cross
   c. Muslims who believed that God is supreme and will reward righteousness but punish wickedness
   d. Spiritual but not religious

6. The _____ Nation of Gods & _____ was started by _____ who left the Nation of Islam in _____. Both "Nations" believed that _____% of the world is blind. _____% are the wealthy and powerful who deceive the masses. And the remaining _____% are the Poor Righteous Teachers who educate the other eightyfive.

7. According to Talib Kweli, who were some popular rappers from the Golden Era that were 5 Percenters? And what did you have to be able to do be considered one of the best during that time?

   (a) Biggy & Tupac   (b) Slick Rick & Kool Moe D.   (c) Big Daddy Kane & Rakim

   You had to be able to _____

8. By "god" they meant ___-___-___-___-___ which stood for _____.

9. Before 1992, only a few rappers, about four or five, on the East Coast had ever put the "N" word in their songs, how do you think the 5 Percenters may have been responsible for this fact?

   _____

   _____

10. In KRS-One's song "The Conscious Rapper" he states, "to be a conscious rapper aint a mystery you gotta laugh when they call you contradictory." Which of the following contradictory things do you think Conscious rappers did during Hip Hop's Golden Age?

        a. They held to a variety of belief systems that conflict with one another
        b. They believed the black man was god but still called him the "N" word
        c. They disrespected women, often only viewing them as sexual objects

How do you think this impacted the way their positive messages was received?

_____

_____

_____

_____

Lesson 8: Gangsta Rap

Aside from Consciousness, another thing that made the Golden Age glow was the fact that rap from a different region of the country was beginning to surface. In fact, the new sounds from the West Coast would forever change rap music and present Hip Hop culture with its first moral crisis.

Student Learning Outcomes: As a result of this lesson, I can
- State the origins and name the originators of what came to be known as Gangsta rap.
- List two differences between East Coast and West Coast rap during the Golden Age

....

Intro

1. They say, 'At first, art will imitate life; but then life will imitate art.' What do you think this means?

   _____

   _____

   _____

2. Do you think art, especially when it comes to rap music, is better when artists create reflections of how things really are; or is it better when artists create things that project how things *should be*? **Explain** your answer.

   _____

   _____

   _____

Diving In - From Gods to Gangstas

1. <u>Gangsta</u> Rap began

   a. On the West Coast in Compton, California (1988)
   b. On the East Coast in the Bronx, New York (1981)
   c. Down South in Atlanta, Georgia (1978)
   d. On the East Coast in Philadelphia, Pennsylvania (1985)

2. The first Gangsta rapper was

   e. Ice Cube
   f. Ice T.
   g. Tupac
   h. Schooly D
   i. Suge Knight

3. On the _____ stage, rappers are talking about _____

   and talking to _____ .

Talking About
• Their Opponents Lack of Skill
• Their Own Skills on the Mic
• The DJ
• Having nice objects
• Bringing Cultural/Social Awareness
• Keeping the Crowd Hype
• Bringing Cultural/Social Destruction
• Having Fun
• Reinforcing Positive Black Identity
• Women as Objects
• Reinforcing Negative Black Identity

Talking To
• Potential Fans
• Party Goers
• Potential Music Buyers
• Other Rappers
• America
• Black-America Specifically

Watch the video for the song "Original Gangster" by Ice T. – 1991 (1st two verses) then answer the following question

1. What stage(s) of rap did Ice T. use to admire? Cite lyrics to support your answer

   _____

   _____

2. Why did Ice T. decide to switch up his style and stop rapping like New York rappers? (Find two reasons)

   _____

   _____

3. Listen to "PSK Making that Green" by Schooly D – 1985 (1st and 2nd verses)

Which Stages? / Cite Lyrics to support	
1st _____	/ _____
2nd _____	/ _____
3rd _____	/ _____
4th _____	/ _____

4. What does Schooly D do in his song that is different from the rest of rap music in 1985?
   a. Talk about using drugs
   b. Brag about his car
   c. Threaten to kill another rapper for biting his style
   d. Use the "N" word to refer to another black man

5. Why did Schooly D's hardcore street style not take off on the East Coast but fit perfectly on the West?

   _____

   _____

   _____

6. Listen to the first two verses of Ice T.'s song "6 in the Morning" and Easy E's "Boys in the Hood" – What are some similarities and some differences between their songs and Schooly D's "PSK"? (name at least two)

Similarities	Differences

7. While promoting the "Straight Out of Compton" movie in 2015, Dr. Dre claimed that the twenty-seven-year-old song "F the Police" was their version of "non-violent protest." Do you think this description fits that song? Yes or No. **Explain**

_____

_____

_____

8. In the movie and in real life, when N.W.A. was asked why they were producing "Gangter rap," Ice cube responded that it was not Gangster rap but _____ -rap.

9. Would you say that N.W.A. was more Black Power or Blaxploitation? **Explain**

_____

_____

_____

10. How can you use the concept of "art imitating life" and "life imitating art" to discusss N.W.A.'s *Straight Outta Compton* album and its impact on Hip Hop?

_____

_____

_____

Outro

1. When Gangsta/Trap/Drill rap artists today claim to be "keeping it real" in their music, they're saying that their art is a reflection of life; but could it be possible that their lives are just a reflection/imitation of someone else's art? **Explain** your response.

_____

_____

_____

_____

2. When it comes to Gangsta rap, is it more important that artist show us how things are or how things should be? **Explain** your answer.

_____

_____

_____

_____

Lesson 9: Peer Preasure and the New Wave

Almost every child has probably heard his/her parents say, "If your friends went and jumped off of a bridge would you do it to?" They say this to challenge young people to 'think for themselves.' But admit it, it is hard to resist the preasure from peers, especially when it seems like everybody else is doing something; and especially if it is working for them. This is when character is most tested and leadership is most needed.

Student Learning Outcomes: As a result of this lesson, I can
- Estimate the impact of Gangsta rap on the broader Hip Hop community
- Summarize and Evaluate the 2nd response of East Coast rappers to Gangsta rap

....

Intro:

1. Has there ever been a cultural trend that you said you would not be a part of, but as time went on, you found yourself doing it along with everyone else? If so, what was the trend and why did you eventually join in?

   _____

   _____

2. Has there ever been a cultural trend that you saw everyone embracing but you were able to reject it **because it was out of your character**? If so, what was the trend and what character trait would you have had to abandon to go along with it? **Expain**

   _____

   _____

   _____

   _____

Diving In - Riding the New Wave

1. At first, East Coast rappers tried to set an example by using violence as a metaphor for something better. But the 2nd response (of some but not all East Coast artists) was to copy the West Coast by

    a. Forming Gangs

    b. Forming super-groups of solo MCs

    c. Using the N-word in their music when they did not do so before

    d. Getting the Jheri Curl hairstyle

2. After beginning in 1973, Hip-Hop music existed for _____ years with virtually no _____.

    a. 5

    b. 10

    c. 15

    d. 20

3. Listen to the first verse of the 1993 song "Sucka N*gga" by A Tribe Called Quest, then answer the following questions:

    a. How do you know the artist is not completely okay with the word he is using?

    _____

    _____

    b. What line best describes why he does not want to use it?

    _____

    _____

    c. What line best describes why he gave in and began using the word?

    _____

    _____

4. Why might it have been especially important for East Coast artists, more than anyone else, to make a good decision about whether or not to use the word in rap music?

    _____

    _____

The "N" Word in the Golden Age of Hip Hop: Use the chart to answer the questions beside

Year	Artist	Album	Total 'N' words	Region
1985	Run DMC	King of Rock	0	East Coast
1985	LL Cool J	My Radio	0	East Coast
1985	Schooly D	Schooly D	15	East Coast
1986	Run DMC	Raising Hell	0	East Coast
1986	2 Live Crew	We Are the 2 Live Crew	0	The South
1987	Public Enemy	Yo! Bum Rush the Show	0	East Coast
1987	KRS One	Criminal Minded	0	East Coast
1987	LL Cool J	Bigger and Deffer	0	East Coast
1987	Too $hort	Born to Mack	3	West Coast
1987	Ice T	Rhyme Pays	1	West Coast
1987	Eric B. & Rakim	Paid in Full	0	East Coast
1988	Geto Boys	Making Trouble	0	The South
1988	KRS One	By All Means Necessary	0	East Coast
1988	Big Daddy Kane	Long Live the Kane	0	East Coast
1988	EPMD	Strictly Business	1	East Coast
1988	Eric B. & Rakim	Follow the Leader	0	East Coast
1988	N.W.A.	Straight Outta Compton	44	West Coast
1988	2 Live Crew	Move Somethin'	69	The South
1988	Slick Rick	The Great Adventures of Slick Rick	0	East Coast
1988	Jungle Brothers	Straight Out the Jungle	0	East Coast
1989	Too $hort	Life is Too Short	4	West Coast
1989	Geto Boys	Grip It! On That Oher Level	43	The South
1989	D.O.C.	No One Can Do It Better	5*	West Coast
1989	Kool G Rap & DJ Polo	Road to the Riches	0	East Coast
1989	EPMD	Unfinished Business	0	East Coast
1989	Big Daddy Kane	It's a Big Daddy Thing	0	East Coast
1990	King Sun	Righteous but Ruthless	22*	East Coast
1990	Above the Law	Living Like Hustlers	8*	West Coast
1990	Public Enemy	Fear of A Black Planet	7	East Coast
1990	Ice Cube	Amerikkka's Most Wanted	52	West Coast
1990	KRS One	Edutainment	8**	East Coast
1990	Paris	The Devil Made Me Do It	3**	West Coast
1990	Brand Nubian	All For One	0	East Coast
1991	Master P	Get Away Clean	41	West Coast
1991	Ice T	Original Gangster	91	West Coast
1991	2Pac	2Pacaly-pse Now	85	West Coast
1992	Eric B & Rakim	Don't Sweat the Technique	0*	East Coast
1992	Redman	What? Thee Album	20	East Coast
1992	Common Sense	Brother Can I Borrow a Dollar	21	Chicago/ East Coast
1992	Kool G Rap & DJ Polo	Live and Let Die	151	East Coast
1993	A Tribe Called Quest	Midnight Marauders	72	East Coast
1993	Snoop Dogg	Doggy-style	135	West Coast
1994	Nas	Illmatic	52	East Coast
1994	Outkast	Southern-playalisticadalacmuzik	113	The South
1994	UGK	Super Tight	190	The South
1994	Common Sense	Resurrection	39	Chicago/East Coast
1994	The Notorious B.I.G.	Ready to Die	102	East Coast

1. What is your first impression (what comes to mind) when you study this chart?

_____

_____

2. Identify two artists/groups who did not use the N-word during or before 1988 and continued to not use it afterward.

_____

3. Identify two artists/groups who did not use the N-word during or before 1988 but began using it during or after that year.

_____

4. Are there any artists/groups who only started making music after 1988 and did not use the N-word? If so who? And what stage were they probably on?

_____

5. As the "N" word became more common in rap music, so did the "B" word and lyrics about robbing, harming or killing other black/brown people. How might the acceptance of the "N" word have caused the increase of all these other ideas? Or, if you think the word had nothing to do with it, how would you explain why all these things increased around the same time?

_____

_____

_____

_____

_____

_____

_____

Listen to the song "Navigating the 'N' Word" by Phanatik and answer the following questions

Verse 1

Black folks die every day/ they die in every way

But some are dying as n*ggas I was dying to say it

As a kid I would play with my friends in my section

We'd pull out the N-word and use it as a weapon

Like "N*GGA!" we'd laugh like playing with a pistol

We didn't think was loaded til we heard that thang whistle

"N*gga!" "Whatchu call me!?!" "N*gga! My n*gga."

Saying it was like pulling a trigger

Cause each time we said it, something in us died

Cause if my n*gga's a n*gga I figure so am I

BLAM!!! BLAM!!! BLAM!!! But we playin'

We don't really mean it/ it's only a saying

That was til that day when dude was getting beat

Every time they slammed his head on the concrete

You what they said right before they hit him

"N*gga!" "Take that! N*gga!" "Get'em!"

He knocked that n*gga out/ that's what that n*gga get

It's like cause he's a n*gga/ killing him's legit

That thang me and my friends joked with was loaded

Now I don't know if I wanna HOLD IT

Chorus

I'm a n*gga/ he a n*gga/ she a n*gga/ we are n*ggas

Wouldn't you like to be a n*gga too?

Cause you can own a n*gga/ beat a n*gga/ kill a n*gga

Steal a n*gga's girl cause that what n*ggas do

When they tryna be like masssta/

N*gga I'ma beat you like masssta

Don't be mad if I treat you like masssta/ cause I just

Wanna Be your masssta/ My N*gga

1. What does Phanatik compare the N-word to in this verse? ALSO underline examples of this comparison.

_____

_____

2. Is it possible that something inside of us could really die each time we use the N-word? If so, what could be dying?

_____

_____

_____

_____

3. What does Phanatik mean by, "If my n*gga's a n*gga I figure so am I?

_____

_____

_____

_____

4. What changed the artist's mind about the N-word being just a "figure of speech"?

_____

_____

_____

_____

Outro

If becoming more gangster, controversal and edgy in their songs helped a lot of inner-city kids get record-deals and sell records, was copying N.W.A.'s use of the "N" word a moral decision for the culture? an immoral one? or is this a matter of opionion and not really a question of right-or-wrong? **Explain** your answer using each of the ethical systems you learned in Unit 3.

_____

_____

_____

_____

_____

_____

_____

Lesson 10: Commentary and Confrontation

In 1990, West Coast rapper Paris made it clear that he was not on the same wave as N.W.A. But disapproving commentary about Gangsta rap came from the East Coast almost immediately after the *Straight Outta Compton* album dropped in the summer of 1988. The criticism and commentary eventually turned into the conflict that became known as the East Coast – West Coast rivalry in Hip Hop.

Student Learning Outcomes: As a result of this lesson, I can
- Name the primary artists responsible for Hip-Hop's first regional rivilry
- Outline the events that led up to the conflict
- Evaluate the moral legitimacy of the underlying issues at the root of the confrontation

....

Intro

1. From what you know about Hip-Hop history, what was the East Coast/West Coast beef about and which side do you believe won?

_____

_____

_____

2. Which side would you have rooted for if you were around back then, and why?

_____

_____

_____

Diving In - East vs. West Pt. 1

1. Hip-Hop's first geographical (territory-based) battle was the East Coast/West Coast rivilry in the 1990's

   True   OR   False

2. One of the very first criticisms thrown from one region across the country to another was

   a. Blahzay Blahzay's song "Danger" aka "When the East is in the House"
   b. The Jungle Brother's album "Straight Out the Jungle"
   c. The Waynes Brother's movie *Don't be a Menace to South Central While Drinking Your Juice in the Hood*

3. The East Coast/West Coast beef began as a battle between which two artist

   a. Ice T. and L.L. Cool J.
   b. Tim Dawg and N.W.A.
   c. Ice Cube and Common (Sense)
   d. The Notorious B.I.G. and Tupac Shakur

Watch the video for the 1991 song "F*ck _____" by _____ then answer the following questions

4. What stage(s) is the rapper on

   Party   Battle   Braggadocious   Conscious   Gangsta

5. What vice did this artist fall victim to and did he have a legitimate reason to? Explain

   _____

   _____

6. Watch the video for the 1994 song "I Used to Love H.E.R." by _____ then answer the following questions

   a. Who is the H.E.R. that the artist is talking about and what lines give it away? (pick at least 2)

      _____

      _____

   b. What lines do you think _____ took exception to (had a problem with) and why?

      _____

      _____

c. What stage of rap is _____ accusing the West Coast/Gangsta rap of putting an end to? And do you believe him when he says it was "cool" for H.E.R. to be on the West Coast and that he's not "salty" about it?

Party   Battle   Braggadocious   Conscious | Yes   OR   No

d. If you were _____ how would you have responded to this criticism?

_____

_____

7. How did this beef end?

a. Common was the bigger man and apologized for offending Ice Cube
b. Ice Cube was the bigger man and admitted he shouldn't have taken it personal
c. After an almost fatal shootout both rappers realized it had gone too far
d. Minister Farrakhan from the Nation of Islam stepped in to broker peace

8. Watch the video for the song "Real People" by Ice Cube and Common then answer the following questions

a. Are there any references to the past beef between these two artists? If so, what lines?

_____

_____

b. What word best describes Ice Cube in the first five bars of his verse?

Excited   Proud   Hopeful   Regret

c. When you add the 6th bar to lines 1 thru 5, what is Ice Cube really saying?

_____

_____

_____

d. Which of the following words best describes bar #7 from Ice Cube and why? **(Circle and explain)**

Sad _____

Ironic _____

Curiosity _____

e. Who is Common referring to as the "gods" in his verse?

_____

_____

Outro

Was the original issue between Ice Cube and Common a moral one where someone was truly right and the other person was truly wrong or was this simply a matter of opinion between the two artist and not really a matter of right-and-wrong? Explain

_____

_____

_____

_____

Unit 3
The Eight Pillars of Culture
- Defining Culture
- How Culture Works
- Defending Hip Hop as Culture
- Cultural Leadership

Overview: It is impossible for people to occupy the same space over long periods of time witout developing a 'culture.' People who are determined to be counter-cultural and even the anti-social will find that they are still linked in undeniable ways to some particular culture. We inherit culture and, at the same time, we advance it as we consume and create more of it. Because of this, it is important that we learn to evaluate the cultures we embrace, and make intentinoal choices about the kind of culture we will produce for those who come after us.

Student Learnnig Outcomes: By the end of this unit, you will be able to
- Define Culture
- Justify the claim that 'Hip Hop is a culture'
- Use the Eight Pillars of Culture to evaluate the strengths and weaknesses of Hip Hop or any other culture

Lesson 1: Defining of Culture

Sometimes we stereotype people based on where they live, the color of their skin or other factors. Our assumptions might very well be wrong, or they could be right, but we feel comfortable making them because of the way culture works.

Student Learning Outcome: As a result of this lesson, I can
- Define Culture
- List the things that 'culture' consists of
- Name at least three different cultures that influence my life and the ways in which they do this

....

Intro

1. Why do you and the people around you dress the way that you dress and talk the way that you talk?

   _____

   _____

2. Is there such a thing as dressing/talking/acting black or white? Explain?

   _____

   _____

   _____

   _____

   _____

   _____

Diving In – This is How We Do It

1. How would you define _____?

    a. Your Definition

    _____

    _____

    a. Simple Definition

    _____

    b. Goodwin's Defintion

    _____

    *From one _____ to the next, the _____ might change but the _____ never do

2. What do people in the same culture usually share?

    (Same culture, same . . .)

    1) _____
    2) _____
    3) _____
    4) _____
    5) _____
    6) _____
    7) _____
    8) _____

3. Can you name some of the cultures that give you answers to these 8 things? List the culture and which pillar that culture provides for you.

    _____   _____

    _____   _____

    _____   _____

    _____   _____

4. Which of the 8 items from question #2 do you think Hip Hop does the best job at giving us? And which the worst? **Give examples**

    Best - _____

    _____

    _____

    Worst - _____

    _____

Outro

- Pick 3 of the cultural items listed in #2 and explain how things might be different if each individual person had his/her own answer to those Pillars. Then choose, which one would be the most difficult to maintain if everyone had their own?

_____

_____

_____

_____

_____

_____

_____

_____

_____

_____

_____

_____

_____

_____

_____

_____

_____

_____

_____

_____

Lesson 2: The Basic Questions

Culture is the distinct way people come together to answer life's questions. Many people do not stop to think about the answers their culture is providing. But perhaps they would if they had a better understanding of the questions being addressed. This is where the real work of cultural study begings.

Student Learning Outcomes: As a result of this lesson, I can
- Name the first two pillas of culture
- Identify in what ways, if any, Hip Hop culture answers these two pillars

....

Intro

If a person does not like the answers to the 8 Pillars that his/her culture is living with, is there anything that can be done or does that person have to live with the answers provided by their culture? **Explain**.

_____

_____

_____

_____

_____

_____

_____

Diving In - Food and Image

1st Pillar

Food (What to _____ and how to _____ ?)

1. Ask two people

  ➢ Person #1 _____
    a. What did you have for dinner last night? _____
    b. What culture does that food come from? _____
    c. Did you eat alone or with family? _____

  Answer for yourself: Where you surprised by a, b, or c? _____
                                What surprised you and why? _____

                                _____

                                _____

  ➢ Person #2 _____
    a. What did you have for dinner last night? _____
    b. What culture does that food come from? _____
    c. Did you eat alone or with family? _____

  Answer for yourself: Where you surprised by a, b, or c? _____
                                What surprised you and why? _____

                                _____

                                _____

2. Does _____ have its own answer to 'food' question(s)? If so, what are some of its answers?

                    _____

                    _____

                    _____

3. If a group of people gets the majority of their answers from another group of people, then they are not a _____, they are a _____ of that other group.

4. As we go through these pillars, do you think we will find Hip Hop to be a culture or a sub-culture?

_____

2nd Pillar

Image (What fashion _____ and _____ set us apart?)

1. Does Hip Hop have its own image? Is so, give some examples?

        _____

        _____

        _____

2. Who wore it best?

        a. What decade in Hip Hop do you think had the _____?

        b. What decade in Hip Hop do you think had the _____?

        c. Could you tell the _____?

3. The first rapper(s) to receive an endorsement deal from a clothing apparel company was

        a. Wu Tang Clan

        b. Nelly

        c. N.W.A.

        d. Run DMC

4. For _____, their fashion was more about

        a. Making money

        b. Being proud of their culture

        c. Showing that they could afford nice things

        d. Being in style

5. In 1995, Tek from the rap group Smif n Wessun rapped that he wears "Timbs all season for a**-kicking reasons." In 2018, **femcee** Young M.A. rapped that she has a "fresh white tee with the constructs on." Were these two artists wearing Timberland boots for the same reason? How do you know?

        _____

        _____

        _____

Listen to the 2005 song, "Self-Conscious" by Kanye West then answer the following questions

1) Which lyric does Kanye use to explain why people in his culture wear jewelry and high-priced fashion?

_____

_____

2) Would you feel better about yourself if your clothes cost $400? Why or why not?

_____

_____

_____

3) What does Kanye mean by the line, "We tryna buy back our 40 acres" and what is ironic about that line?

_____

_____

_____

4) Kanye says that "The people highest up got the lowest self-esteem." Why do you think that might be?

_____

_____

_____

_____

5) Would you feel worse about yourself if your sneakers only cost $9.99? Why or why not?

_____

_____

_____

Outro

1. In Shakespeare's play *Hamlet*, Polonius gives his son this advice: "Spend whatever you can afford on clothes but make sure they're quality, not flashy, since clothes make the man." What do you think he means by the last four words and is this true?

_____

_____

_____

2. In the case of early Hip Hop, did their clothes make them _____ or did they make their clothes _____. And how is this the same or different from the way people view fashion and image today?

_____

_____

_____

_____

_____

_____

_____

_____

_____

Lesson 3: Dialect and Art

Cultures set themselves apart by what or how they eat and what they wear. But if you listen and look you can detect cultural indicators in other key ways.

Student Learning Outcomes: As a result of this lesson, I can

- Explain the role dialect plays in marking and maintaining culture
- Describe a unique facet of the dialect of Hip Hop culture
- Critique art from three different perspectives

....

Intro

1. Have you ever created a new term (including slang) that you believe everyone else started saying after you? If so, what is that word/term and what does it mean?

_____

_____

2. Try to come up with a new slang word now, on the spot. And see if you can get anyone else to agree to begin using it.

_____

_____

Diving In – Spoken Words, Artists

3rd Pillar

Dialect (How do we make _____ easier for those in our group while keeping

_____ at bay?)

Pin the Tale on the Decade

#1	#2	#3	#4	#5	#6
a. 1850's	a. 1960's	a) 1870's	a) 1870's	a. 1960's	a. 1850's
b. 1950's	b. 1970's	b) 1970's	b) 1970's	b. 1970's	b. 1970's
c. 1980's	c. 1980's	c) 1980's	c) 1980's	c. 1980's	c. 1980's
d. 1990's	d. 1990's	d) 1990's	d) 1990's	d. 1990's	d. 1990's

_Not _____ meaning _____ but _____ meaning _____!_

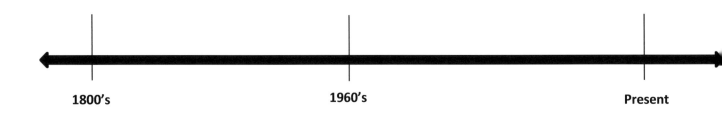

1800's   1960's   Present

1. Are the following situations a case of bad meaning _____ or bad meaning _____?

    a. Black Lives Matter movement disrupts traffic to protest the justice system _____

    b. A black student disrupts the classroom while a white teacher is trying to teach _____

    c. A black woman is ordered to 'move back and stop recording' a police officer who is making an arrest. She moves back but does not stop recording. _____

    d. A black man cannot find a job so begins selling perscription pills and heroin _____

2. Hip Hop slang changes often, why do you think that is?

       a. because it's trendy and that's just how trends work

       b. because parents start using it and kids don't want to use the same slang as adults

       c. because white people start using it and it loses its "cool"

       d. because a lot of it comes from the criminal world and they don't want cops catching on

3. Listen to the 1998 song, "Ebonics" by Big L, then answer the following questions.

       a. Does the artist mention any slang terms that people still use today? Name 3.

             _____

             _____

             _____

       b. Are there any slang terms that you've never heard but you think are clever enough to begin using? If so, name 2.

             _____

             _____

       c. What do you think Big L's answer would be to question #2 above? How do you know and can you find any examples in the song?

             _____

             _____

             _____

4. What are the similarities and differences between the dialect of slaves and the dialect of Hip-Hop culture?

Similarities	Differences
_____	_____
_____	_____
_____	_____

4th Pillar

Art (*What's* _____ and *Why*? And *How* _____ can it be done.

a) The first question is about the _____ of a particular work of art.

b) The second question is about the _____ of the artist on the _____ .

c) The third question is about the _____ of a particular work of art.

    1. Between these three, which do you find yourself most concerned with when listening to music?

        Style   or   Subject   or   Stance

    2. Which question is most important overall?
        Explain your choice

        _____

        _____

        _____

1. Watch the video for the the 1992 song, "They Want Efx" by Das Efx (1st verse) then answer the following questions.

    a. On a scale of 1 to 10 (1 being the worst and 10 being the best), what would you give these artists on having a good subject?

        1 2 3 4 5 6 7 8 9 10

    b. Can you tell what was worth reproducing to the artists of this 1992 hit song? What was the subject?

        _____

        _____

    c. Now that you know what the subject of this song was, what would you give these artists on having a good

        Subject 1 2 3 4 5 6 7 8 9 10

        Style   1 2 3 4 5 6 7 8 9 10

        Stance   1 2 3 4 5 6 7 8 9 10

2. There are at least three ways to create art or "answer the Cultural Pillar" of art.

   a. Art: Straight-up –The artists highly values the subject and has reproduced it in a good light. The stance is that others should _____ .

   b. Art in *Reverse* – The artist is showing what he/she does _____ . The stance is that others should _____ it either but instead, _____ the opposite.

   c. Art as an *Interview* – Instead of the artist choosing a _____ and expressing a clear _____ , it is left unclear so that you get to _____ .

3. If you had to guess, why did _____ think that his life/culture in South Central L.A. was not worth reproducing on the Big Screen?

   _____

   _____

4. Watch the clip from the 1991 movie *Boys in the Hood,* then answer the following question.

   What would the stance of the film be if it was taken as each of the following forms of Art?

Straight-up: _____

In Reverse: _____

As an Interview: _____

5. Which of these three styles do you think it was *and* is there anything from the clip that could support your answer?

   _____

   _____

   _____

   _____

Outro

Watch the video for the 2018 song, "This is America" by Childish Gambino, then answer the following question?

- What is the subject? (what did the artist reproduce)
- What was the artist's stance on the subject? (if he gave one)
- Or was it 'Art as an interview' (if so, what is the message you get from the song/video)

_____

_____

_____

_____

_____

_____

_____

_____

_____

_____

_____

_____

_____

_____

_____

_____

Lesson 5: Values

The deeper we dive into the Eight Pillars of Culture, we can see how the questions get begin to tie together. That is especially the case when it comes to considering a culture's values.

Student Learning Outcomes: As a result of this lesson, I can
- Explain the importance of cultural values
- List at least three examples of cultural values
- Evaluate at least three of the values of Hip Hop culture

....

Intro

1. What are some things that make life worth living for you?

   _____

   _____

   _____

   _____

   _____

   _____

2. How do you protect those things or ensure that those things will be around tomorrow and the next day?

   _____

   _____

   _____

   _____

Diving In – You Know How We Do It

5th Pillar

Values (How do we _____, Perpetuate, and _____ our way of life?)

1. What are some things that you and the people in your culture would fight for together and even die for?

   _____

   _____

   _____

   _____

2. In a 1963 speech, Dr. Martin Luther King Jr. said, "If a man hasn't discovered something that he will die for, he isn't fit to live." How could 'having something worth dying for' impact the way a person lives?

   _____

   _____

   _____

   _____

3. What are _our_ values? On a scale of 1 – 5, how much do these groups value the following things?

   (1) = Miss me with that!   (2) = If I have to, then okay ☹   (3) = In theory, yes

   (4) = That's _that_ stuff!   (5) = Try to stop me

	Worth living/Dying for	America's Values	Hip Hop Values	My Values
1	Freedom			
2	Happiness/Pleasure			
3	Strong Family Unit			
4	Information/Knowledge			
5	Safety/Protection			
6	Law & Order			
7	Self-Respect			
8	Respect by Others			
9	Money/Material Things			
10	Justice			

4a. Are there any things that you think America should value more or less than it does?

More   Less

_____   _____

_____   _____

_____   _____

4b. Are there any things that you think Hip-Hop should value more or less than it does?

More   Less

_____   _____

_____   _____

_____   _____

4c. Are there any things that you believe you should value more or less than you do?

More   Less

_____   _____

_____   _____

_____   _____

5. From the values listed in the chart above, choose two and give an example of how they might conflict with one another. Do this at least three times.

Example: <u>Freedom</u> <u>vs.</u> <u>Safety</u>   <u>Right to carry, but now anyone can have a gun anywhere</u>

Conflicting Values   **Scenario/example?**

1) _____ vs. _____   _____

2) _____ vs. _____   _____

3) _____ vs. _____   _____

When it comes to Hip Hop culture, which values do you think compete the most?

1) _____ vs. _____   _____

2) _____ vs. _____   _____

6. Cultures are made up of people who agree on the answers to most of the Eight Pillars. If a group of people values the following things, what will they put in place to protect or preserve them?

       a. Liberty/Freedom they would put in place _____.

       b. Justice they would put in place _____.

       c. Order they would put in place _____.

       d. Knowledge they would put in place _____.

       e. Family they would put in place _____.

7. Does Hip Hop culture value _____? How many rap songs can you think of that talk about it in a positive way?

   _____

   _____

8. When rappers brag about being sexually intimate with somone elses' girlfriend/baby-mom/wife, what does it say about their value of family and commitment and what are they valuing more?

   _____

   _____

   _____

9. Could there be a connection between Hip Hop culture's views on _____ and the state of family-life in the inner-city? **Explain**.

   _____

   _____

   _____

   _____

   _____

   _____

   _____

   _____

10. Watch the video for the 1990 song "Love's Gonna Get'cha" by KRS One then answer the following questions.

    a. What are some things the main character in this song valued in the first verse (cite lyrics to support your answer)

_____

_____

_____

    b. As the song went on, did his values change? If so, what did they change to. If not, explain why you'd say 'no.'

_____

_____

_____

    c. Do you think money changes people or does it just reveal who the person really is? **Explain**.

_____

_____

_____

    d. Do you think that you overuse the word "love". If so, what are some things that you say you love but probably should choose a different word for?

_____

_____

_____

    e. Compare this song with the 2018 song "Die Poor" by J-Jon. What are the similarities in the message and what are the differences?

_____

_____

_____

119

f. Which is worse: dying _____ money OR dying _____ money? **Explain**.

_____

_____

_____

_____

_____

Since When?

In what decade did the following things become values in Hip-Hop culture?

1. Rap skills
   a. Since the beginning   b. 1980's   c. 1990's   d. 2000's
2. Money/material things
   a. Since the beginning   b. 1980's   c. 1990's   d. 2000's
3. Crime/drugs/no snitching
   a. Since the beginning   b. 1980's   c. 1990's   d. 2000's
4. Swag over Substance
   a. Since the beginning   b. 1980's   c. 1990's   d. 2000's
5. Women as sexual objects
   a. Since the beginning   b. 1980's   c. 1990's   d. 2000's
6. Doing Jail-time
   a. Since the beginning   b. 1980's   c. 1990's   d. 2000's
7. Being a 'bad-n*gga'
   a. Since the beginning   b. 1980's   c. 1990's   d. 2000's
8. Unity and having fun
   a. Since the beginning   b. 1980's   c. 1990's   d. 2000's
9. Black on Black crime
   a. Since the beginning   b. 1980's   c. 1990's   d. 2000's
10. Anti-police
   a. Since the beginning   b. 1980's   c. 1990's   d. 2000's

Outro

When values conflict with one another, the best thing to do is to prioritize them. From the box below, choose the things you value and put them in order from most to least important. Then list one thing you can do to protect/preserve each thing and one character trait you will need to accomplish this.

Freedom	Family	Fun	Faith
Health	Future	Education	Love
Safety	Self-respect	Street-cred	Money
Happiness	Comfort	Fashion	People's Respect

	Value	**How can you safeguard it**	**Character**
1st	_____	_____	_____
2nd	_____	_____	_____
3rd	_____	_____	_____
4th	_____	_____	_____
5th	_____	_____	_____
6th	_____	_____	_____
7th	_____	_____	_____
8th	_____	_____	_____
9th	_____	_____	_____
10th	_____	_____	_____

Cultural Values: Auxiliary Lesson

Listen to the 1st verse of the 2010 song, "We Can Be More" by Sho Baracka, then answer the following questions

1. In the first line, the artist says that his relationship is "way past lust." What is the difference between love and lust?

   _____

   _____

   _____

2. Write the line from this song that best describes marriage to you, and explain your choice?

   _____

   _____

   _____

3. Why do you think this artist is embarrassed by his "playboy past"?

   _____

   _____

   _____

4. Which of the following best describes marriage to you?

   a. Just a piece of paper
   b. Important for a healthy society
   c. A fairytale; not realistic

   _____

   _____

   _____

5. Do you think you can separate fatherhood from marriage without negative consequences?

   _____

   _____

   _____

Listen to the 2012 song, "Daughters" by Nas, then answer the following questions

1. Nas was a thug and a "pimp" and now he wants his daughter to end up with someone just like him.

    True   or   False

1.a- Which lyric helped you to answer #1?

_____

_____

2. Nas sees himself as a pretty decent parent with no regrets.

    True   or   False –

2.a- Which lyric(s) help you to answer #2?

_____

_____

3. Should Nas expect his daughter to want to date someone who is different than the type of man he was while she was growing up and watching him? Why or why not?

_____

_____

4. Which values do you think were in competition for Nas' when his daughter was young?

Freedom	Safety	Money	Pleasure
Equality	Justice	Law/Order	Happiness
Knowledge	Family		Self-Respect
Respect from Others	Land/Houses		Success

_____

_____

_____

_____

5. Which values are competing the most in your life right now. Explain how? (keep it G...rated)

_____

_____

_____

Lesson 6: The Ultimate Questions

Even though all the pillars of culture are based on questions that groups of people are attempting to answer together, there are certain questions that rise to the level of ultimacy. These questions have always mattered a great deal, even though their answers are some of the most debated topics in all of life.

Student Learning Outcomes: As a result of this lesson, I can
- List the Ultimate Questions and explain what makes them so "ultimate"
- Name two sources people tend to go to for answers to the Ultimate Questions
- List the various answers Hip Hop culture has embraced to these questions

....

Intro

Who is the most spiritual rap artist you know of and what has he/she done to convince you of their spirituality?

_____

_____

_____

_____

Diving In – You Ain't Got the Answers

6th Pillar

Ultimate Questions (What is our _____, _____, and _____ and How do we _____?)

1. Which of those three things do you think is most important to know and why?

   _____

   _____

   _____

2. Why do you think these are called ultimate questions?

   _____

   _____

3. In the past, where do you think most people would turn to find answers to the Ultimate Questions?

   _____

   _____

4. In today's world, where do people turn in order to get answers to these questions?

   _____

5. Are there any Ultimate Questions that _____ can answer? If so, what would be the answer given?

   _____

6. Are there any Ultimate Questions that _____ cannot answer? If not, why not?

   _____

   _____

7. During the Golden-age of Hip Hop, which belief system did most rappers lean on to get answers to the Ultimate Questions?

   a. Islam
   b. Christianity
   c. They were Spiritual but not Religious
   d. 5 Percent Nation of Gods and Earths

125

8. Listen to Jay Electronica's 2009 song "Exhibit C" and answer the following question.

How many references to the teaching of his belief system are in the song? Write them below.

_____

_____

_____

_____

_____

_____

_____

_____

9. When Hip Hop moved to the south, which belief system did most rappers lean on to get answers to the Ultimate Questions?

   a. Islam
   b. Christianity
   c. They were Spiritual but not Religious
   d. 5 Percent Nation of Gods and Earths

10. Watch the video for the 2015 song "Illmind 7" by Hopsin, then answer the following questions.

   a. Based on the lyrics, what problems does Hopsin have with religion? (Name 3)

   _____

   _____

   _____

   b. Do you see Hopsin's expression as being disrespectful to God or as a sincere quest for religious truth? **Explain** your answer.

   _____

   _____

   _____

   _____

c. Towards the end of the song, Hopsin says that he will only stop living sinfully if God proves to be real. Is 'God being real' the only reason to live a life of morals and values? If yes, explain why. If not, what are some other reasons?

_____

_____

_____

_____

d. What are some of Hopsin's *values* that he believes he cannot hold while being a Christian. List at least 3 *and* **Cite lyrics** to support your answer.

_____

_____

_____

_____

_____

_____

_____

_____

e. Does Hopsin provide answers to any of the Ultimate Questions? If so, what answers does he give?

_____

_____

_____

_____

Outro

Do you think Hip Hop would be better or worse if more artists shared their views on answers to the Ultimate Questions? Explain why you feel this way. And, if you can, name at least 3 artists who do this on a consistant basis?

_____

_____

_____

_____

_____

_____

_____

_____

_____

_____

_____

_____

_____

_____

Lesson 7: Icons

Every culture has people who stand out; people who have done something to make their entire group take notice of them. Without these individuals, it is hard to imagine where, or even if, the culture would be. If you're looking for someone who embodies the best of what a group of people has to offer (and sometimes, the worst), search for and study their icons.

Student Learning Outcomes: As a result of this lesson, I can
- Define and differentiate between cultural heroes and cultural idols
- Compare the concept of heroes and villains to the role of rappers within Hip Hop culture

....

Intro

1. Who are some of your personal heroes and what makes them a "hero" in your eyes?

_____

_____

_____

_____

_____

_____

_____

_____

_____

_____

2. Is there a difference between an idol and a hero? If so, how would you explain that difference?

_____

_____

_____

_____

_____

7th Pillar

Icons (Who are the visionaries, leaders, _____ and idols that _____ for giving us our answers to the first six pillars?)

1) In American culture, what names come to mind when it comes time to answer the first six pillars?

Food _____   Art _____

Fashion _____   Values _____

Dialect _____   Ultimate Questions _____

2) The difference between an idol and a hero is that

_____

_____

_____

3) Are the following people idols or heroes? And which pillars do they provide answers to?

Michael Jackson (idol or hero) _____ (which pillars) _____

Meek Mill (idol or hero) _____ (which pillars) _____

Michelle Obama (idol or hero) _____ (which pillars) _____

Montana 300 (idol or hero) _____ (which pillars) _____

Michael Jordan (idol or hero) _____ (which pillars) _____

Martin Lawrence (idol or hero) _____ (which pillars) _____

Martin Luther King Jr. (idol or hero) _____ (which pillars) _____

Missy Elliot (idol or hero) _____ (which pillars) _____

Mandela (idol or hero) _____ (which pillars) _____

McDonald's (idol or hero) _____ (which pillars) _____

4) Are most of the rappers in your playlists cultural idols or heroes?

_____

5) Why might a person desire to go from being a cultural idol to a cultural hero **and** what are some "pros and cons" of doing so?

_____

_____

_____

_____

_____

_____

6) Listen to the 1st verse of the 2013 song "Let Nas Down" from J. Cole and answer the following questions.

   a. How does J. Cole view Nas and what lyric helps you answer that question?

   _____

   _____

   b. Why did J. Cole have a hard time understanding what Nas told him back stage?

   _____

   _____

   c. How did J. Cole let Nas down and should Cole have cared? Would you have if you were him? Why or why not?

   _____

   _____

   _____

   _____

   _____

   _____

7) Listen to the 2013 song "Let Nas Down Remix" by Nas and answer the following questions.

    a.   Why do you think Nas mentions his young-boy days in this song?

_____

_____

    b.   What does Nas say usually happens when he tries to give advice to young artists and how is J. Cole different? (What character trait is present in this scenario?)

_____

_____

    c.   Have you ever had an experience where someone tried to give you advice and you didn't listen, but then you ended up regretting it? Explain if you can.

_____

_____

_____

_____

8) Watch the video for the 2018 song "Old N*ggas" by YBN Cordae and answer the following questions.

    a.   J. Cole had attempted to do for the younger generation what Nas did for him. How was the response he got different from what happened between him and Nas?

_____

_____

_____

    b.   Is Cordae's song a dis? And is the title/content of this song disrespectful to older rappers in the game? **Explain**

_____

_____

_____

_____

c. Which one(s) of the first 6 Pillars of Culture does Cordae have a problem with when it comes to the older generation and which character trait(s) is he basically accusing them of lacking? (Cite lyrics to support you answer)

_____

_____

_____

_____

_____

_____

_____

_____

_____

9) If a culture has heroes, then it also has _____. These are people who are well-known for _____ the culture's _____.

10) If an artist consistently raps about shooting black and brown people, selling drugs, pimpin' hoes and disrespecting other members of his/her culture, do you think that that person should be considered culturally heroic or villainous in Hip Hop? (is that person violating the values of the culture?) **Explain**.

_____

_____

_____

_____

_____

_____

_____

_____

Outro

1. Are there any cultural idols (or villains) that you have been treating like heroes?

   Yes   OR   No

2. What are the dangers of treating cultural idols (or villains) like heroes? Name at least two and **Explain** your answer.

   _____

   _____

   _____

   _____

   _____

   _____

   _____

   _____

   _____

   _____

   _____

   _____

   _____

   _____

   _____

   _____

   _____

   _____

   _____

   _____

Auxiliary Lesson: Cultural Heroes

Watch the "Emerald City Sequence" from the 1978 movie, *The Wiz* then answer the following questions.

1. Which of the 8 Pillars of Culture can you detect in these lyrics? **Give examples.**

_____

_____

_____

_____

_____

_____

_____

2. Find three examples of Dialect **and** write what you think they mean.

_____

_____

_____

3. Do you think the residents of Emerald City saw the Wiz as a cultural idol or hero? **Explain your choice.**

_____

_____

_____

4. Would **you** consider the Wiz an idol or a hero? **Explain your choice.**

_____

_____

_____

5. The *style* of this art is Story-telling, Musical, Movie, Re-make, Allegorical

    a. What is the *subject* of this particular scene? _____

    b. What *stance* is the artist talking on the subject? _____

_____

_____

Lesson 8: Historic Events

When asked why an artist of his stature still made time to perform at events like Hot 97's Summer Jam in New York City, Jay Z replied, 'Because, I understand that without memorable moments to look back at together, cultures die out.' That statement is not just about making new memories, it is about commemorating the moments that have sustained us until now.

Student Learning Outcomes: As a result of this lesson, I can

- Demonstrate how the 8th pillar of culture is connected to the other pillars and which it is connected to the most.

....

Intro

How many Holidays can you name? (only list the Holidays for now)

1) Holiday_____ Hero _____ Pillars _____

2) Holiday_____ Hero _____ Pillars _____

3) Holiday_____ Hero _____ Pillars _____

4) Holiday_____ Hero _____ Pillars _____

5) Holiday_____ Hero _____ Pillars _____

6) Holiday_____ Hero _____ Pillars _____

7) Holiday_____ Hero _____ Pillars _____

8) Holiday_____ Hero _____ Pillars _____

9) Holiday_____ Hero _____ Pillars _____

10) Holiday_____ Hero _____ Pillars _____

11) Holiday_____ Hero _____ Pillars _____

12) Holiday_____ Hero _____ Pillars _____

13) Holiday_____ Hero _____ Pillars _____

14) Holiday_____ Hero _____ Pillars _____

15) Holiday_____ Hero _____ Pillars _____

16) Holiday_____ Hero _____ Pillars _____

17) Holiday_____ Hero _____ Pillars _____

18) Holiday_____ Hero _____ Pillars _____

19) Holiday_____ Hero _____ Pillars _____

20) Holiday_____ Hero _____ Pillars _____

Diving In – Hip Hop Hooray

8th Pillar

Historic Events (What are the _____ when we received answers to the other Pillars of Culture?)

1. Most holidays are set up to commemorate heroes who gave new answers to the pillars of _____ and _____.

2. Does Hip Hop culture have any historic events? If so, what are they?

    _____

    _____

    _____

3. Why do you think it is that Hip Hop as a culture does not have any actual, national holidays?

    _____

    _____

    _____

4. In the song "What We Do" Philadelphia rapper Beanie Sigel rapped, "Real gangsters make hood holidays." If Hip Hop did have any actual holidays, what do you think one would be? (What would it be called? What Pillars would it be based on? Who would the heroes be? How would it be celebrated?)

    _____

    _____

    _____

    _____

    _____

5. Watch the video for the 1992 song "Hip Hop Hooray" from Naughty by Nature then answer the following questions.

    a. What is the subject of this song and what is the artists' stance on the subject?

    _____

    _____

b. Do the artists have any conflicting values that they express in the song? If so, name them and cite lyrics to support your answer.

_____

_____

_____

_____

_____

_____

_____

_____

Auxiliary Lesson: Cultural Integrity

The Eight Pillars of Culture are

1. **Food** (What to eat and how to prepare it, serve it, eat it?)
2. **Image** (What fashion statements and standards set us apart?)
3. **Dialect** (How do we make communication easier for those in our group while keeping outsiders at bay?)
4. **Art** (What's worth reproducing? And Why? And how skillfully/uniquely can this be done?
5. **Values** (How do we preserve, Perpetuate and Progress our way of life?)
6. **Ultimate Questions** (What is our Origin, Meaning, and Destiny. And how do we know?)
7. **Icons** (Who are the visionaries, leaders, heroes and idols who are known for answering the first six pillars?)
8. **Historic Events** (What are the monumental moments when these questions were answered for us?)

....

1. Are there any Pillars that Hip Hop does not have its own answers to? If so, which ones?

   _____

   _____

   _____

2. Based on the definition given in lesson One of this unit, is Hip Hop a culture?
   Yes   OR   No *and* Why or why not?

   _____

   _____

   _____

3. If you wanted to weaken someone's culture, which of the 8 Pillars could you give them poor answers to in order to do the most damage. **Explain**.

   _____

   _____

   _____

   _____

   _____

4. It is possible for someone to be giving answers to two or more pillars at the same time? Can you think of any examples of this? Try coming up with two separate examples

   e.g. For instance, someone making or wearing a tee-shirt with a religious phrase on it has just combined which two pillars, at least? _____ and _____ .

   You try:

   #1
   _____

   _____

   _____

   _____

   #2
   _____

   _____

   _____

   _____

5. Watch the video of Chuck D. then answer the following questions.

   a. Which pillars did Chuck D. combine to give answers to his culture?

      _____

      _____

   b. Why do you think so many people today still do what Chuck D did even though they don't know why he did it or even who he is? And what pillars do you think are involved?

      _____

      _____

      _____

      _____

Unit 4
Ethics

- Defining Morality
- Defining Ethics
- Ethical Systems
- Ethical Choices

How do we know the difference between right and what is wrong? Most of us are taught as children but who taught the people who taught us? And who taught the people who taught them? Who was the first person to determine that something was right and the opposite of that was wrong and, what if they were…wrong? In order to make decisions about *morality*, we need to have an understanding of *ethics*.

Student Learning Outcomes: By the end of this unit you will be able to

- Differentiate between ethics and morals
- Explain the relationship between ethics and morals
- Define three ethical systems and Decide which will take priority when you are faced with moral choices

Lesson 1: Good to Know

If there were no rules in your school, at your job or in your city, how long would it take before everything turned to chaos? Or do you think people could be trusted to know and do what was right even without rules? Is "what's right" free to change from person to person, culture to culture and even over time? Are there any things that are always right or always wrong no matter where or when they happen? Wouldn't all of this be good to know?

Student Learning Outcomes: As a result of this lesson, I can

- Define morality
- Explain the need for ethics

....

Intro

1. Do you think most people are naturally good or naturally bad? Explain if you can.

   _____

   _____

   _____

2. Think about infants and toddlers, do you usually have to teach them to be good or teach them to be bad? And what does this mean for you answer to question #1?

   _____

   _____

3. What do you think comes more naturally, the virtues or the vices? And what does this mean for you answer to #1?

   _____

   _____

   _____

Diving In – What's Really Good?

Directions: Fill in the blanks then answer:

1. *Morality* – The idea that there is *really* such a thing as _____ & _____ and therefore, _____ & _____ .

2. Do you believe that there is really such a thing as good and evil/right and wrong? Or do you think those things are just a matter of opinion?

_____

3. Scenario #1 is:

    a. Right   b. Wrong   c. Nasty but not a matter of right and wrong

4. Scenario #2 is:

    a. Right   b. Wrong   c. Creepy but not a matter of right and wrong

5. If you had to use a synonym for the word "good" but could not use the word "right", what other word(s) might you use instead?

_____   _____

_____   _____

_____   _____

_____   _____

6. The most common words to replace "good" and "right" are _____ , _____ and socially-_____ .

7. How are these three terms different?

    a. _____ means that something is _____ good.

    b. _____ means that something is allowed by _____ .

    c. Socially-_____ means that something is considered good by the majority of people in a certain society.

Decide if the following actions should be considered *Immoral*, *Illegal* or just *Socially Unacceptable*

1) Taking someone's pen when they go to the bathroom

   Immoral   Not Immoral but Illegal   Just Socially Unacceptable

2) Eating your 3rd, and the last slice of pizza when someone else in the room hasn't had any yet

   Immoral   Not Immoral but Illegal   Just Socially Unacceptable

3) Jay-walking

   Immoral   Not Immoral but Illegal   Just Socially Unacceptable

4) A parent breaking a promise to a child

   Immoral   Not Immoral but Illegal   Just Socially Unacceptable

5) A president breaking promises to the nation

   Immoral   Not Immoral but Illegal   Just Socially Unacceptable

6) Cheating on your boyfriend or girlfriend

   Immoral   Not Immoral but Illegal   Just Socially Unacceptable

7) Cheating on your husband or wife

   Immoral   Not Immoral but Illegal   Just Socially Unacceptable

8) Texting while Driving

   Immoral   Not Immoral but Illegal   Just Socially Unacceptable

9) Showing an R rated movie to a minor

   Immoral   Not Immoral but Illegal   Just Socially Unacceptable

10) Showing pornography to a minor

   Immoral   Not Immoral but Illegal   Just Socially Unacceptable

11) Morality is _____

   Ethics is _____

   So, your M_____ is _____ on your E_____.

Moral Dilemmas

Watch the video for the song "'Guilty Conscience" by Dr. Dre and Eminem, then answer the questions below

1. Dr. Dre tells the man who is about to rob the store to think about the consequences if he gets caught; he also tells him to think about the wellbeing of the old lady in the store. Which of these two reasons would be more convincing to you and why?

_____

_____

_____

2. Eminem tells the robber that the old woman doesn't care about him and his kids, so he shouldn't care about her: Is that a good point? Explain.

_____

_____

_____

3. Do you think that everyone has a conscience like the people in this song OR do you think that some people are just "savage," with only one voice, a negative one, in their head? **Explain**.

_____

_____

_____

....

Outro

Can you trust your "gut" to tell you what is right or wrong? Have you ever had a situation when your "gut" was telling you two different things? How did you decide in that case?

_____

_____

_____

_____

Lesson 2: Ethical Systems

Even though we have laws in our country, people usually don't consult them to find out what is right and wrong. Instead, often without even knowing it, we use different ethical systems to decide if certain actions are moral or immoral.

Student Learning Outcomes: As a result of this lesson, I can

- Name at least three different ethical systems
- State what makes them different
- List their strengths and weaknesses

....

Intro

Think for a moment: How do YOU decide what's right and what's wrong?

_____

_____

_____

Diving In – For Good Measure

Ethics – refers to the systems used to _____ between right and wrong. It answers the question, 'How do we _____ what's right and wrong?'

1) The first ethical system we will look at is called 'Ethical _____.'

    a. A decision is 'right' if the good will outweigh the bad for _____.

    b. A decision is 'wrong' if the bad will outweigh the good for _____.

       i. If a person is an **Egoist**, is cheating on boyfriend/girlfriend: Right or Wrong???

_____

Pros	Cons
1. _____	1. _____
2. _____	2. _____
3. _____	3. _____
4. _____	4. _____
5. _____	5. _____

      ii. If a person is an **Egoist**, is stealing a pair of Beats when no one is looking: Right or Wrong??? _____

Pros	Cons
1. _____	1. _____
2. _____	2. _____
3. _____	3. _____
4. _____	4. _____
5. _____	5. _____

iii. If a person is an **Egoist**, is stepping in when a stranger is being bullied: Right or
       Wrong??? _____

Pros	Cons
1. _____	1. _____
2. _____	2. _____
3. _____	3. _____
4. _____	4. _____
5. _____	5. _____

Ethical Egoism

Strengths	**Weaknesses**

2) The second ethical system we will look at is called _____ Ethics.

    a. A decision is 'right' if the good will outweigh the bad for the _____.

    b. A decision is 'wrong' if the bad will outweigh the good for the _____.

        i. If a person is an **Utilitarian**, is Cheating on boyfriend/girlfriend: Right or Wrong??? _____

Pros	Cons
1. _____	1. _____
2. _____	2. _____
3. _____	3. _____
4. _____	4. _____
5. _____	5. _____

       ii. If a person is an **Utilitarian**, is stealing a pair of Beats when no one is looking: Good or Bad??? _____

Pros	Cons
1. _____	1. _____
2. _____	2. _____
3. _____	3. _____
4. _____	4. _____
5. _____	5. _____

iii. If a person is an **Utilitarian**, is stepping in when a stranger is being bullied:
      Right or Wrong??? _____

Pros	Cons
1. _____	1. _____
2. _____	2. _____
3. _____	3. _____
4. _____	4. _____
5. _____	5. _____

Utilitarian Ethics

Strengths	Weaknesses

3) The third ethical system we will look at is called '_____ Ethics.'

Right and Wrong has already been established by _____ or_____
Law.

    i.   If a person is **Deontological**, is cheating on boyfriend/girlfriend: Right or Wrong??? _____

Pros	Cons
1. _____	1. _____
2. _____	2. _____
3. _____	3. _____
4. _____	4. _____
5. _____	5. _____

    ii.   If a person is **Deontological**, is stealing a pair of Beats when no one is looking: Good or Bad??? _____

Pros	Cons
1. _____	1. _____
2. _____	2. _____
3. _____	3. _____
4. _____	4. _____
5. _____	5. _____

iii. If a person is **Deontological**, is stepping in when a stranger is being bullied: Right or Wrong??? _____

Pros	Cons
1. _____	1. _____
2. _____	2. _____
3. _____	3. _____
4. _____	4. _____
5. _____	5. _____

Deontological Ethics

Strengths	Weaknesses

Outro

Which of these 3 ethical systems do you operate according to the most? Give at least 1 example

_____

_____

_____

_____

_____

Lesson 3: Motives – Consider the Source

We usually esteem people who go beyond Ethical Egoism and show concern for more than just themselves. In fact, when people go so far as to commit selfless (Altruistic) acts for the good of others, we call them "heroes." But if we only look at the "hero's" actions, it is not always easy to tell which ethical system he/she is using.

Student Learning Outcomes: As a result of this lesson, I can

- Distinguish between 'good motives' and 'good actions'
- Use 'motives' to determine which ethical system a person is operating by

....

Intro

1. If someone does the right thing but for the wrong reason, have they just done good or bad?

   e.g. A student compliments a teacher, hoping to get a better grade on an assignment.

   _____

   _____

2. If someone does the wrong thing but for the right reason, have they just done something good or bad?

   e.g. Joining a violent gang for protection in a violent neighborhood

   _____

   _____

3. What percentage of whether something is 'right or wrong' depends on the outcome of a person's actions and what percentage of it depends on the motives behind the action?

   Outcome _____%   Motives _____%

Diving In – Heroes or Nah?

Ethical systems and moral choices show up in the media all the time. Consider how the following cases relate to the three ethical systems discussed in the previous lesson.

1. Watch the Spider-man movie clip then discuss and answer the following questions.

a. If Spider-man is an Ethical Egoist – What will he do in this scenario and why?

_____

_____

_____

b. If Spider-man is a Utilitarian Ethicist – What will he do in this scenario and why?

_____

_____

_____

c. If Spider-man is a Deontological Ethicist – What will he do in this scenario and why?

_____

_____

_____

2. Watch the Batman movie clip then discuss and answer the following questions.

a. If the people on each boat are all Ethical Egoists – What will they do in this scenario and why?

_____

_____

_____

b. If the people on the boats are Utilitarian Ethicists – What will they do in this scenario and why?

_____

_____

_____

c. If the people on the boats were Deontological Ethicist – What will they do in this scenario and why?

_____

_____

_____

Ethical Systems & Hip Hop

1. Which system is Biggie using in the song referenced

     Egoism   Utilitarian   Deontological

2. Which system is J Cole using in the song referenced

     Egoism   Utilitarian   Deontological

3. Which system is Nicki using in the song referenced

     Egoism   Utilitarian   Deontological

4. Which system is Freeway using in the song referenced

     Egoism   Utilitarian   Deontological

5. In the beginning, most of Hip Hop's Deontological artists were

    a. Muslim
    b. 5 Percenters
    c. Christian
    d. Spiritual but not religious

6. Today, there are 5 Percent, Muslim and Christian rappers. What do all of these have in common?

_____

7. In the _____ God made the first man a _____, to teach him that "good" meant _____.

8. According to Genesis, part of the purpose of mankind is to create as much _____ as possible without letting anything unnecessary _____.

Outro

Listen to the song "Jesus Walks' by Kanye West. On a scale of 1 to 5 (one being 'not a at all' and five being 'very much so') how much of an Egoist, Utilitarian and Deontological ethicist is Kanye? Explain your answer using song lyrics and your own opinion of those lyrics.

Lesson 4: Personal Ethics

Every day, we use a variety of ethical systems to determine whether we ourselves or the people around us are in the right or in the wrong. There are more systems you could study, but the three we have looked at are some of the most common. Often, these systems can work to support one another.

Student Learning Outcomes: As a result of this lesson, I can

- Identify which ethical system I currently subscribe to most
- Identify the system I most desire to live by
- Explain what *Character Development* has to do with being an ethical person.

....

Intro

Which ethical system would you use 1st, 2nd and 3rd to decide if the following choices were right or wrong? Indicate the order by writing 1st, 2nd or 3rd beside the appropriate letter for the three systems. (Put an "X" if not at all)

1. Stealing when no one else is around

   E _____   U _____   D _____

2. Selling one's body or drugs to feed the family

   E _____   U _____   D _____

3. Paying Taxes

   E _____   U _____   D _____

4. Cursing out a teacher

   E _____   U _____   D _____

5. Shoveling your neighbor's sidewalk

   E _____   U _____   D _____

6. Sex outside of marriage

   E _____   U _____   D _____

7. Shooting two people who jumped your cousin

   E _____   U _____   D _____

Personal Ethics Questionnaire

(Answer for yourself as best you can)

1) At this stage of my life, I am more of a _____
   a. Ethical Egoist
   b. Ethical Utilitarian
   c. Deontological Ethicist

2) I wish I was more of a _____
   a. Ethical Egoist
   b. Ethical Utilitarian
   c. Deontological Ethicist

Why? _____

3) I want the people that I hang out with to be _____
   a. Ethical Egoist
   b. Ethical Utilitarian
   c. Deontological Ethicist

Why? _____

4) I want the person I fall in love with to be _____
   a. Ethical Egoist
   b. Ethical Utilitarian
   c. Deontological Ethicist

Why? _____

5) If/when I have children, I will raise them to be _____
   a. Ethical Egoists
   b. Ethical Utilitarian
   c. Deontological Ethicists

Why? _____

6) Pick two character traits that, if you had them, would either make it easier or harder for you to be the kind of ethical person you chose for #2 above. Explain your answer.

_____

_____

_____

Made in the USA
Middletown, DE
12 October 2021

49779133R00091